DO-IT-YOURSELF BIBLE STUDIES

ROMANS

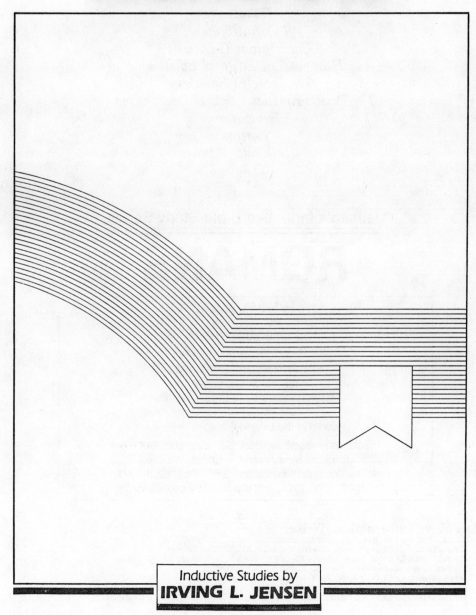

Inductive Studies by
IRVING L. JENSEN

Here's Life Publishers, Inc.
San Bernardino, California

Other books available in the Irving Jensen Do-It-Yourself Bible Study Series

Jensen's Inductive Bible Study Series

ROMANS

by Irving L. Jensen
Published by
HERE'S LIFE PUBLISHERS, INC.
P.O. Box 1576, San Bernardino, CA 92402

Fifth Printing, November 1989
ISBN 0-89840-036-8
©1983, Here's Life Publishers, Inc.
All rights reserved
Printed in the United States of America

Unless otherwise indicated, Scripture quotations are
from the New American Standard Bible,
©The Lockman Foundation 1960, 1962, 1963, 1971,
1972, 1975, 1977, and are used by permission.

For More Information, Write:
L.I.F.E.—P.O. Box A399, Sydney South 2000, Australia
Campus Crusade for Christ of Canada—Box 300, Vancouver, B.C., V6C 2X3, Canada
Campus Crusade for Christ—Pearl Assurance House, 4 Temple Row, Birmingham, B2 5HG, England
Lay Institute for Evangelism—P.O. Box 8786, Auckland 3, New Zealand
Campus Crusade for Christ—P.O. Box 240, Colombo Court Post Office, Singapore 9117
Great Commission Movement of Nigeria—P.O. Box 500, Jos, Plateau State Nigeria, West Africa
Campus Crusade for Christ International—Arrowhead Springs, San Bernardino, CA 92414, U.S.A.

CONTENTS

PREFACE

The Bible is as contemporary as today. When the Holy Spirit first inspired Paul to write Romans, He intended the readers to be the saints at Rome (1:7) *and also you.* This is why the letter to the Romans was made part of a book that will never grow old or go out of print—the BIBLE.

So the invitation and challenge to study Romans is in your hands. What you do with this opportunity is bound to affect your life, whether you are a Christian already, or not a believer.

This study guide is geared mainly to the Christian student, since Romans was written to Christians. But the letter is also for the non-Christian. If you are not a believer as you begin to study Romans, you are urged to have an open heart and mind to what God has for you in His Book. The Holy Spirit wants to speak to you.

The New American Standard Bible

Why is the *New American Standard Bible* (NASB) the text used for these DO-IT-YOURSELF study guides?

This question is answered best by identifying the objectives of the Bible Studies. Here are the main objectives:

1. To make a detailed study of the Bible book, carefully analyzing its paragraphs and segments (groups of paragraphs).

2. To identify with the Bible authors as closely as possible by finding the answers to these questions: "What are you saying?" and "What do you mean?"

3. To learn not only *what* the Bible author wrote (content), but *how* he wrote it (form). Once these things are discerned, we are ready to ask him: "*Why* did you write it?"

4. To apply the Bible text to our personal living, as it originally was intended by that author.

The NASB supports those objectives in the following ways:

1. It is a precise, accurate translation of the original languages. F.F. Bruce says: "It retains many of the features of the ASV [*American Standard Version*, 1901], especially that precision of rendering which made that version so valuable for *detailed textual study.*"[1] Regarding its accuracy, William S. LaSor writes that it is "exceptionally faithful to Hebrew and best Greek texts."[2]

2. The precision of the NASB translation lends itself to a breakdown of its phrases and lines into a "talking text." This gives the student an excellent view of *how* the original author arranged what he was inspired to write.

3. The NASB, though far from the King James in its literalness, is nevertheless the most literal of the modern versions. It is not paraphrastic and casual, yet the text is in clear, readable contemporary English. This allows the serious Bible student to make accurate OBSERVATIONS in the course of his study.

Notice where the NASB stands in the following comparative list of major English Bible versions, moving from the very literal to the very paraphrastic (from my book *How to Profit From Bible Reading,* p. 24):

1. *New King James Version* (NKJV, 1982)
2. *New American Standard Bible* (NASB, 1971)
3. *Revised Standard Version* (RSV, 1952)
4. *New Berkeley Version in Modern English* (Modern Language Bible) (MLB, 1959)
5. *New International Version* (NIV, 1978)
6. *Good News Bible* (Today's English Version) (TEV, 1976)
7. *New English Bible* (NEB, 1970)
8. *Jerusalem Bible* (Roman Catholic) (JB, 1966)
9. *New Testament in Modern English* (Phillips) (Phillips, 1958)
10. *The Living Bible* (TLB, 1971)

Conclusion: Today we are blessed with having many good Bible versions. I have found the NASB to be the best version for the analytical studies of this DO-IT-YOURSELF series. As you study the UNITS, the text of other versions (e.g., the excellent *New International Version*) will be cited for clarification or alternate reading.

FOOTNOTES

1. "Bible Versions and Bible Enjoyment," *Eternity Magazine,* 1974, page 42.
2. *Ibid.*

INTRODUCTION

The fruits of Bible study depend in large measure upon how determined a student is to learn and to grow spiritually. Read the following statements and grade your own mind-set regarding each of them. Now is the time to set or confirm your priorities.

1. I want to study the Bible.

2. I want to study the Bible conscientiously.

3. I am willing to work hard and to spend the necessary time.

4. I expect my Bible study to be profitable, with the Lord's help (2 Tim. 3:16-17).

The remainder of this introduction focuses on the practical side of Bible study, such as methods and tools. Bible study demands effort, but when you use the proper tools carefully, *Bible study works*, and it is enjoyable!

Suggestions for Study

Everyone has questions about how to study the Bible, and rightly so. Below are three basic questions, and this author's answers.

1. *Where do I begin?*

Someone has said, "Study the Bible the way God wrote it—book by book." (The chronological sequence is not intended here—in fact, we do not know the *exact order* of the writing of the 66 books of the Bible.) So the answer to the question is, "Begin with a whole book of the Bible." The book you choose depends on your needs and desires.

Let us say you have chosen a book for study. Now what do you do? The answer involves three different activities, in this order:

a. BACKGROUND—learning the book's background, such as author, date and purpose. This is a brief study *about* the book. (See pages 12-13.)

b. SURVEY—scanning the book's text from beginning to end, in a sweeping, general, skyscraper view. This brief study gives you a feel of the book, and provides context for the analytical studies that follow. (See pages 13-14.)

c. ANALYSIS—moving slowly through the book,

unit by unit, scrutinizing the words and phrases as to their meanings, relationships and intended applications. Most of your Bible study should be this kind of analysis.

The practical length of a unit for analytical study is a segment, which is a group of paragraphs. A segment is usually shorter than a chapter. For your convenience, each unit of this study guide represents one segment.[1]

2. *How should I study?*

What method or procedure should I use?

This study guide recommends the inductive method, which is a natural approach for all Bible students to take. Inductive Bible study is *independent* study,[2] for, as much as possible, you are examining the text yourself. Your personal experience and enjoyment is in discovery, because you come to the passage as though you had never seen it before and, in studying it, you let it speak for itself.

What the Bible says, you *observe*. So OBSERVATION is the first stage of inductive study. After that, you are interested in finding out what that observed truth *means*. That is INTERPRETATION, the second stage. Now you are ready to *apply* the text which you observed and to which you assigned meaning. This is the final stage of all Bible study, APPLICATION. (Refer to Unit 1 and note where the three stages of observation, interpretation and application appear.)

3. *What helps should I use?*

a. First, depend on the Holy Spirit who is your best teacher and guide. He inspired the text in the beginning, and one of His main ministries is to instruct each believer in whom He dwells.

b. For the most part, don't resort to outside helps (e.g. commentaries) during the OBSERVATION stage of your study process, for your most fruitful and exciting experiences will come from what you do *on your own*. Among other things, you will observe that the Bible text usually answers the very questions it may raise.

c. This study guide is designed to make your

Bible analysis more effective without its doing the studying for you. Its purposes include pointing out paths of searching, maintaining a momentum and offering a minimum of content and commentary to complement your independent study. A recommended companion to use along with this guide is this author's previously written work on *Romans* (Moody Press).

How to Use This Study Guide

The text of Romans has been divided into 43 segments, each of which is a unit in the structure of the epistle. So your analysis of the book will involve 43 lessons, or units of study. In this study guide each numbered study unit appears on two facing pages, so that you do not turn a page during the course of each lesson. Follow the directions given below, for each study unit.

1. The overall pattern of your study should move from left to right on the facing pages.

2. Observe at the top of the pages what the Bible passage is, and the title assigned to it, suggesting its theme. During the course of your study you may want to assign a different title.

3. Read the SETTING description at the top of the left page, to be reminded what brought on the present passage in the progress of doctrinal instruction.

4. Refer to the survey chart of Romans and note where in Romans the passage of your study unit appears. The shading shows the location. This preliminary exercise is intended to help you recognize the *context* of your passage.

5. Read and study carefully the textual re-creation of the Bible text (NASB) as it appears in the chart of the left page. The master title of each page is determined from one key phrase of that text and is identified this way:

The "talking text" preserves the thought patterns of the Bible text, to help you in the observation stage. The two main things it shows are *emphases* and *relationships* of words and phrases. These are the best clues to what the author is writing. For *emphasis*, a word may be shaded, or printed in large letters, or circled. The *relationship* between two phrases may be made by a connecting line, or similar print, or similar location.

6. Move now to *Key Words and Phrases.* Have pencil in hand for marking and recording. Read the text again, and mark the words and phrases you think are the key ones in the segment. Things which identify *key* quality include: repetition, importance (e.g., a strong doctrinal phrase like "died for you"), sharpness, uniqueness, cruciality. As a starter, one key word is shown for each unit. Record others that you see, using the suggested verse locations.

7. Read the *Segment Survey,* referring to the charted text as you read, so you will get acquainted with the entire segment before examining the parts.

8. Now you are ready to launch into the main part of the OBSERVATION stage, the Paragraph Analysis. You will move paragraph by paragraph, as indicated. Record answers to questions when these are called for. Some questions are simple yet basic; for example, Who? What? When? How? and Why? Use notebook paper to record extensive answers.

9. Note the list of *Related Verses.* Derived from other parts of the Bible, these relate to the subject of your present passage. Read them in your Bible and record their main parts in the spaces provided or on separate paper. You will have reason to refer to these on your own at different times in the three stages of your study (OBSERVATION, INTERPRETATION, and APPLICATION).

10. Now that you have seen what the Bible text says, you are ready to think about what it *means.* This is the INTERPRETATION stage. Since the Bible is its own best interpreter, you will find that many, if not most, of your interpretations will come from your observations of the Bible text. When questions are given in this section, answer them to the best of your ability, using the Bible text as the basis for your answers. This is the inductive part of your interpretative study, but much of this section contains brief, helpful commentary on things not answerable from the text. Nevertheless, your own inductive study remains as the important part of this section.

11. The APPLICATION stage is the goal of all Bible study. When you reach this practical part of your study, read the textual re-creation again. This time, observe how you can apply its words and phrases (e.g. commands), especially to your own life. Write the applications in your own words, similar to this: "I should pray often for my weaker brother in the Lord." Use notebook paper to record applications when more space is needed.

If you have read Bill Bright's *Ten Basic Steps Toward Spiritual Maturity,*[3] you will be alert to areas of Christian living, such as prayer and witnessing, which need constant strengthening and encouragement by the Word. Sometimes in this study guide, reference to one of the *Ten Basic Steps* will be made with a notation like this: TBS#4.

12. The purpose of the two parts, *Summary of Passage* and *A Memory Verse,* is twofold. First, it lets you take one final, brief look at the passage you have just studied. Second, it lets you carry away with you at least one memorized verse.

13. The last section, *Looking Ahead,* introduces the subject of the next unit. When you thank the Lord for His help in studying a completed unit,

pray for His continued illumination as you move to the next unit.

Suggestions for Leaders of Group Bible Studies

Group Bible study can be thoroughly enjoyable and spiritually productive if a few basic-guidelines are followed. Group members will learn valuable Bible study skills and communication skills, too, as they share their insights, questions, and life-impacting decisions with one another.

1. *Organize Your Group Carefully and Prayerfully*

Ask God to direct you to several persons who want to develop a deeper relationship with the Lord through group Bible study. These may include new Christians, friends at work, neighbors, or fellow students. Tell them specifically why you want to form a Bible study group; stress the non-threatening, friendly aspects of the meetings; and indicate the place and time of the study. Assure each prospect that the spiritual benefits to be obtained through this kind of Bible study are outstanding.

Generally, six to ten persons comprise an effective group. Each session should be held in an informal setting: a comfortable living room, a private room in a restaurant, or a dormitory room. Light refreshments may be served at either the beginning or close of the study session.

How you arrange the seating is crucial. Ideally, each group member should be able to see everyone else in the group. So, if possible, arrange chairs in a circle or semi-circle. Discussion will be aided by seating a timid person directly across from an outgoing person. Use name tags on chairs to provide whatever seating arrangement you feel would be best to promote good group interaction.

2. *Build a Supportive Atmosphere*

Spend a few minutes at the beginning of each session as a get-acquainted time. Encourage your students to talk about their victories and concerns. Ask two or three persons to pray with praise and requests based on these victories and concerns.

Convey to the group the assurance that no comment or question raised during a session will be ridiculed or ignored. Students should feel secure about entering into discussion as cherished and respected members of the group. Thank your students for participating and compliment them on their openness and their learning. If you find that someone has a tendency to dominate discussions, you may find it helpful to make the rule: "No one may answer more than two questions consecutively without giving another person the opportunity to respond."

Conclude each session with a brief summary of your group's progress—what was learned and how the group plans to apply the truths gained from the study. This will give everyone a sense of accomplishment as well as a sense of accountability to be doers of the Word.

3. *Serve as a Discussion Leader*

Your role in group Bible study is that of a discussion leader. A wise discussion leader does not lecture throughout a session, nor does he act as the expert answer-man. Instead, he relates to the group in a manner similar to that of a coach to his team. Just as a coach helps to develop his players' skills and motivate them, so a discussion leader shows his students how to study the Bible and apply it to daily living. Further, a discussion leader motivates his students to study the Bible diligently and enthusiastically.

4. *Lead Your Group Through Each Section of Every Lesson*

These instructions are based upon the students' doing the assignments during the group Bible study session. However, the assignments are readily adaptable to a do-it-at-home-first system, if you prefer.

Setting

Ask a student to read this "Setting" section aloud from the study guide. Then, direct the group's attention to the organizational chart so they will see where this setting fits into the whole course. Ask if anyone needs further clarification of the setting before you proceed to the next section.

Key Words and Phrases

Instruct the group to read the Bible text silently. It is given in full in the study guide. After reading it, each person should determine its key words and phrases and write these in the "Key Words and Phrases" section. Answers may vary, so don't be alarmed by the different opinions. Ask for volunteers to tell why they made the selections they recorded. The important aspect of this assignment is that your students conceptualize what is happening in the text and think about its significance.

Segment Survey

This section provides some secure pegs on which your students can fasten their grasp of the passage or segment of Scripture. Help them to think through the question(s) in this section. Let volunteers share their answers and tell why they answered as they did.

Paragraph Analysis

It is important to study Scripture paragraph by paragraph, for this helps to see everything in context. Fanciful interpretations, as well as other wrong interpretations, are likely to experience a quick death when a student understands the context of a passage.

Since assignments are more enjoyable when served in bite-size chunks, let the students proceed through the "Paragraph Analysis" section one paragraph at a time, sharing answers and discussing each paragraph.

Related Verses

As your students complete this section, they can see at a glance how Scripture compares with Scripture, and how each passage reinforces the message of the segment under study. Encourage your students to tell how each verse relates to the Bible text.

Interpretations

In this section, the group will find helpful explanations, and they will be able to do some serious thinking about what is being taught in a passage of Scripture. Let your students share their answers. Also, if they wish to raise questions of their own, based on this passage, let them do so. And, whenever possible, let the answers to these questions come from the group.

Applications

Here the mind and heart team up to meet issues, needs, and concerns of daily life. Challenge the group to answer each question thoughtfully, relating it to their own lives. Encourage them to make a few firm decisions about implementing what they have learned. They each should ask themselves:

"How can this information change my attitudes?"

"What changes should I make in my life, based on this information?"

"What specific things can our group do for God's glory, based on what we have learned today?"

You may wish to ask the group to set a few spiritual goals, then call for progress reports in succeeding study sessions.

Summary of Passage

Ask a student to read this section out loud, or ask the group to summarize the Bible text in their own words.

A Memory Verse

Learning a verse of Scripture in connection with each passage studied is excellent spiritual discipline. Take a few minutes of each session to accomplish this. Congratulate those who commit the verse to memory.

Looking Ahead

Before you conclude the study session, refer your students to the "Looking Ahead" section so they will anticipate the next segment of the course.

Time Frame

How much time your group devotes to each

section of a lesson depends upon whether the write-in assignments are done at home or during the sessions. The following time frame is suggested for the latter. Be flexible in altering the time slots to fit the preference of your group.

SECTION	TIME
Setting	3 minutes
Key Words and Phrases	6 minutes
Segment Survey	5 minutes
Paragraph Analysis	30 minutes
Related Verses	10 minutes
Interpretations	10 minutes
Applications	15 minutes
Summary of Passage	4 minutes
Memory Verse	5 minutes
Looking Ahead	2 minutes
Total	**90 minutes**

BACKGROUND OF ROMANS

Romans is the sixth book of the New Testament canon, and it is the first epistle (letter) to follow the historical books (the gospels and Acts). Of the 27 New Testament books, 21 are epistles, and Paul wrote 13, possibly 14, of those. For this reason alone one can understand why Paul has always been regarded the church's chief apostle.

Common to all the New Testament epistles was the writer's and readers' spiritual bond in Christ. So each letter was an appropriate channel for sharing personal testimony, as well as interpreting and applying the grand truths of the gospel.

A. Author of Romans

The opening verse of the letter identifies the author: "Paul, a bond-servant of Christ Jesus, called as an apostle, set apart for the gospel of God." The following sketch of the man and his ministry is supplied by the New Testament text.

1. Paul, the Man

Paul (his Hebrew name was Saul) was born about the time of Jesus' birth, in the city of Tarsus. His father was a strict Pharisee who raised him in that religious setting (Acts 22:3; 26:5). As a youth, he received rabbinical training at Jerusalem under the highly respected teacher, Gamaliel (Acts 5:34; 22:3). Afterward, he probably served in synagogues outside Palestine, and returned to Jerusalem sometime after Christ's ascenscion.

Paul had heard of Christ's teaching, and he was disturbed that many followers were banding together in a new fellowship called the "Way" (Acts 22:4). Since he considered Jesus a false prophet, he joined with other Pharisees in their effort to wipe out this threat to Judaism (Acts 26:9-11). But soon he took the lead in persecuting the Christian church.

Paul's conversion to Christ came at the height of his opposition to the church, on the road to Damascus (Acts 9:1-19a). For the next 14 years God was preparing him for his leadership role, and in A.D. 47 he embarked on his first missionary journey. From that time to his execution in A.D. 67 he was never idle in the ministry of the gospel. Involved in Paul's countless opportunities for service were three missionary journeys, the writing of 13* New Testament books, and many ministries as a prisoner in Rome.

2. Paul, the Writer

Paul wrote nine New Testament letters to churches, and four letters to individuals. The listing of our New Testament canon keeps the two groups intact:

Letters to Churches	Romans
	1 and 2 Corinthians
	Galatians
	Ephesians
	Philippians
	Colossians
	1 and 2 Thessalonians
Letters to Individuals	1 and 2 Timothy
	Titus
	Philemon

The letters to the *churches* focus on (1) the visible church, which is the local church; and (2) the invisible church, which is the universal body of all believers since the church began.

The message of Paul's letters to *individuals* applies especially to individual Christians, concerning Christian living and service.

Woven into all the letters to churches is the clear doctrinal teaching about salvation and Christian living, and Romans is the prominent example of this. Listed first in the New Testament canon, Romans stands as the foundational epistle of the doctrines of salvation. It shows man as lost in sin, hopeless, helpless. It also shows how God, by His mighty power, transforms this unpromising material into living stones of which the church is built, Christ Himself being the chief cornerstone.

B. **Place and Date of Writing**

Paul wrote Romans from Corinth toward the end of his third missionary journey (Acts 18:23–21:17), around A.D. 56.

C. **Original Readers**

The letter was addressed to the saints in Rome (1:7), a mixed fellowship of Jews and

Gentiles, with the latter group probably constituting the majority (cf. 1:13; 2:17). Actually, these Christians did not worship in one church location, but in various homes and other meetingplaces. Having migrated to Rome from various parts of the Mediterranean world, some of these Christians no doubt were converts of Paul's and Peter's itinerant ministries. It is also possible that included in the number were "visitors from Rome" (Acts 2:10) who had been present at Jerusalem on the day of Pentecost and had returned to Rome with the message of Christ. Paul had not yet visited Rome when he wrote the epistle.

D. **Occasion and Purpose of Writing**

Paul's underlying purpose of writing this letter was to pave the way for a personal visit by giving instruction regarding basic truths of salvation—for example, how to be saved and how to live the Christian life.

E. **Theme**

Two key verses of Romans (1:16-17) show that the theme of the book centers about God's salvation offered to man. Paul knew that the darkness of the world—political, social, moral, religious—is not the invention of a pessimist. Instead, it is real and tragic, a condition brought about by the sinfulness of man. If there is any hope, it does not originate in man. It must come from a righteous, all-powerful, and loving God.

The gospel message is God's good news to all people, "for it the power of God for salvation to everyone who believes..." (1:16). This was the message Paul was inspired to write about in Romans. Surely he must have reflected often on his own conversion to Christ, as he composed the letter.

SURVEY OF ROMANS

The rule of study of a book of the Bible is first to survey it as a whole, for overall impressions, and then analyze its individual parts, for detailed observations. In the next few paragraphs you will be given a skyscraper view of Romans, in a deductive approach, before you begin your own first-hand, inductive, analytical study of all the small segments of the book.

A. **Main Features and Overall Structure**

Refer to the accompanying survey chart as you read the observations and descriptions. Note: This survey chart will appear in each unit of your analytical studies to show you the location of the unit's passage in the scope of the whole book.

---

*The number is 14 if he wrote Hebrews.

Book of Romans: GOD'S SALVATION FOR SINNERS						
P R O L O G U E	NEED OF SALVATION	WAY OF SALVATION	LIFE OF SALVATION	SCOPE OF SALVATION	SERVICES OF SALVATION	E P I L O G U E 1:16; 27
	DOCTRINAL				PRACTICAL	
	GOD'S POWER	GOD'S GRACE	GOD'S HOLINESS	GOD'S SOVEREIGNTY	GOD'S GLORY	
1:1	1:18	3:21	6:1	9:1	12:1	15:14

1. Romans has 16 chapters. Scan the pages of your Bible and note the comparative lengths of the chapters.

2. The first 17 verses form Paul's salutation and introduction to the whole book (1:1-17). This may be called a PROLOGUE.

3. The last two segments (15:14-33 and 16:1-27) are Paul's personal messages and benedictions. We call this an EPILOGUE. Observe the prologue and epilogue on the chart.

4. Note on the chart that the main body of the epistle contains two parts: DOCTRINAL AND PRACTICAL. Which is longer? Why should the practical division come *after* the doctrinal? Read the opening verse of each in the Bible text.

5. How does 11:36 conclude the doctrinal section? What is there about 12:1 that suggests the beginning of the practical section? How does 15:13 serve as a conclusion?

6. There are five sections in the body of Romans. The chart shows two outlines: one on salvation, and one on attributes of God. These are listed below, along with additional outlines. Study these carefully, as you look for the progression of thought in Paul's exposition of the subject of salvation. (For example, what is the movement from sin to glory?)

OUTLINES OF ROMANS

1:18–3:20	SIN	God's holiness in condemning sin	NEED OF SALVATION
3:21–5:21	SALVATION	God's grace in justifying sinners	WAY OF SALVATION
6:1–8:39	SANCTIFI-CATION	God's power in sanctifying believers	LIFE OF SALVATION
9:1–11:36	SOVER-EIGNTY	God's sovereignty in saving Jew and Gentile	SCOPE OF SALVATION
12:1–15:13	SERVICE	God's glory, the object of service	SERVICE OF SALVATION

7. The first three sections show a natural unity: (1) why we need to be saved; (2) how to be saved; (3) what the new life of the saved ones is. Logically, the next section would be (5) how to serve God—which is the practical division of the book. Paul "inserts" section (4) in its location because he has more doctrinal things to write about Israel, *before* beginning the practical division.

B. Key Words and Verses

Paul uses the following key words in Romans: salvation, law, righteousness, faith, believe, sin, death, flesh, all, impute, in Christ, Spirit. Look for other key words.

Because of the key words which are part of 1:16-17, these verses serve as key verses for the epistle. In the course of your analytical study you will observe other verses which could have this label.

C. Title

As noted earlier, the central theme of Romans is the imparting of God's righteousness to the sinner who believes on the Lord Jesus Christ. So the suggested title appearing on the survey chart is "God's Salvation for Sinners."

D. Some Prominent Subjects

The prominent subjects of Romans explain why one scholar has said, "A thorough study of this epistle is really a theological education in itself." A rewording of the book's outline identifies some of those subjects: the whole world condemned (1:18–3:20); justification (3:21–5:21); sanctification (6:1–8:39); Israel (9:1–11:36); Christian conduct (12:1–15:13).

FOOTNOTES

1. The version used for these studies is the *New American Standard Bible*—NASB.

2. For further descriptions of the inductive approach in Bible study, see this author's books, *Independent Bible Study* and *Enjoy Your Bible* (Moody Press).

3. Bill Bright, *Ten Basic Steps Toward Christian Maturity* booklets or *A Handbook for Christian Maturity*—a compilation of the TBS booklets (Here's Life Publishers).

PROLOGUE
1:1-17

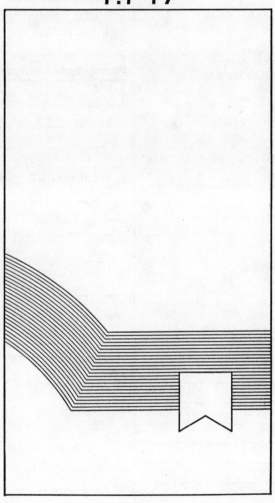

SETTING This is Paul's salutation to his Christian friends in Rome. While it is his personal greeting, it includes an introduction to the theme of the whole letter. Note on the survey chart that 1:1-17 is called PROLOGUE.

Book of Romans: GOD'S SALVATION FOR SINNER

P R O L O G U E	NEED OF SALVATION	WAY OF SALVATION	LIFE OF SALVATION	SCOPE OF SALVATION	SERVICES OF SALVATION	E P I L O G U E 15:1 16
		DOCTRINAL			PRACTICAL	
	GOD'S POWER	GOD'S GRACE	GOD'S HOLINESS	GOD'S SOVEREIGNTY	GOD'S GLORY	
1:1	1:18	3:21	6:1	9:1	12:1	

THE PROMISED GOSPEL

1 PAULBR,
　　(1) a BOND-SERVANT of Christ Jesus,
　　(2) called as an APOSTLE,
　　(3) SET APART
　for the GOSPEL of God
2 　　which He promised beforehand
　　　(1) through His prophets
　　　(2) in the holy Scriptures,

(margin: PAUL)

3 concerning HIS SON,
　(1) who was a descendant of DAVID
　　according to the **flesh,**
4 (2) who was declared
　　THE SON OF GOD with power
　　by the resurrection from the dead,
　　according to the SPIRIT of holiness,
　　JESUS CHRIST OUR LORD,
5 (3) through whom we have **received**
　　GRACE and APOSTLESHIP
　　to bring about the **obedience of faith**
　　among all the
　Gentiles, for His name's sake,
6 　　among whom YOU ALSO ARE THE CALLED
　　of Jesus Christ;

(margin: THE SON)

7 TO ALL who are
　　(1) beloved of God
　　(2) in Rome,
　　(3) called as saints:
　　GRACE to you and
　　PEACE
　　from God our Father and
　　the Lord Jesus Christ.

(margin: SAINTS AT ROME)

OBSERVATIONS
Key Words and Phrases

1:1　"bond-servant"
　1　*apostle*
　1　*set apart*
　4　*Son of God*
　4　*Jesus Christ Our Lord*
　5　*Grace*
　6　*You also Are The Called*
　7　*To all (believers)*
others: 5 ② *Apostleship*
　　③ *obedience of faith*
　　① *received*

Segment Survey

The core of the salutation is three words long.
Complete the phrase: PAUL, TO *All* .
The salutation covers three paragraphs. Who is the main subject in each? *Paul*
Jesus
Saints

Paul
Jesus
Saints

How many sentences are there in the segment? What does this tell you about Paul's style of writing, and about the content?
One - tough, thick, rich, condensed

Compare the first word of the segment with the last. *Paul → Christ*
He always led to Christ

Paragraph Analysis

1:1-2
1. What three things are said about Paul?
Bond-servant
apostle
Set apart for the Gospel

2. What four things are said about the gospel?
1) It's of God
2) promised beforehand
3) thru prophets
4) thru scriptures

3. How is Paul related to the gospel?
He was set apart specifically for the Gospel ('to share)

1:3-6
1. Write down the different things Paul says about Jesus. *David's descendant*
Son of God
Resurrected
He is our Lord

2. What three pronouns refer to believers:
v. 4 *our*
v. 5 *we all*
Do you think "we" refers to Paul, the Christians at Rome, or all of them?
we refer to Paul, etc
v. 6 *but V. 6 says all were called*

16

3. What does Paul write about Christians in the paragraph? *They are called to bring the good news to all*

4. Note the references to the three Persons of the Trinity. What is the context of each?
God - Father
Son - Son resurrected
H.S - according to H.S. the Son is raised

1:7

1. How are the believers at Rome identified?
loved of God
called saints

2. What attributes of God do you see here?
Sovereign, full of grace & mercy, powerful

Related Verses

Matt. 12:18 *Jesus was called, chosen & loved by God + commissioned for gospel*

Mark 16:15 *Gospel t/b preached everywhere to everyone.*

Rom. 9:4-5; 11:13 ff. _____

2 Tim. 2:8 _____

Heb. 1:3 _____

Phil. 4:21 _____

INTERPRETATIONS

1. Write down what you think is involved in these aspects of Paul's ministry (1:1):

bond-servant – *forever*

apostle – *Paul saw Christ & realized what his own mission was to be*

called – *destiny*

set apart – *specially "conditioned" for his mission*

2. What phrases of the second paragraph teach the humanity and deity of Jesus?
humanity *according to the flesh*
deity *powerfully resurrected*

3. What did Jesus' resurrection reveal about Him? *It was how He was declared the Son of God*

4. How does verse 5 associate your ministry with Paul's? *I am a Gentile*

5. What does it mean to be "called by Jesus Christ" (v. 6)? *We have been chosen to be His*

6. What is a saint (v. 7)?
Those loved by God (ie obedient of faith V.5)

APPLICATIONS

1. How can Christians minister as bond-servants of Christ in the work of the gospel?
Share Him with others. Point others to Him

2. All believers are called saints, clothed in Christ's righteousness. What kind of lives should saints live? *Holy lives always being obedient*

3. As a believer, you are "called by Jesus Christ." Do any obligations rest on your shoulders because of this? If so, what kinds? See 1 Peter 2:9. (TBS # 8) Write a list, and check those you are fulfilling. Determine in your heart that you are going to be faithful in all the obligations which you know are yours.

Summary of Passage

Paul, Christ's bond-servant and apostle, greets the saints at Rome. He identifies himself with them as the called of Jesus Christ, the Son of God. And he magnifies Him as the central Person of the gospel.

A Memory Verse 1:1

Looking Ahead

Paul shares his personal testimony about preaching the gospel, and he tells the Christians at Rome how much they mean to him.

17

SETTING Paul wants to assure his Christian friends at Rome that he keeps them close to his heart. Also he wants them to know how eager he is to preach the gospel. So he writes about these things first in his letter.

Book of Romans: GOD'S SALVATION FOR SINNERS

P R O L O G U E	NEED OF SALVATION	WAY OF SALVATION	LIFE OF SALVATION	SCOPE OF SALVATION	SERVICES OF SALVATION	E P I L O G U E 16:27
		DOCTRINAL			PRACTICAL	
	GOD'S POWER	GOD'S GRACE	GOD'S HOLINESS	GOD'S SOVEREIGNTY	GOD'S GLORY	
1:1	1:18	3:21	6:1	9:1	12:1	15:14

PREACHER OF THE GOSPEL

8 First, I thank my God
                              through Jesus Christ
      for you all,
    because YOUR FAITH is being proclaimed
                throughout the **whole world**.
9 For God, whom I **serve**
           (1) in my spirit
           (2) in the preaching
                    of the GOSPEL of His Son,
  IS MY WITNESS
    as to how **unceasingly** I make mention of you,
10   **always** in my prayers making request,
    if perhaps now at last
        by the WILL OF GOD
        I may succeed in **coming to you**.

(margin: THANKFUL)

11 For **I long to see you**
    in order
    (1) that I may impart some SPIRITUAL GIFT to you,
12   (2) that you may be ESTABLISHED; that is,
    (3) that I may be ENCOURAGED together with you
                  while among you,
    each of us by the **other's faith**,
        both yours and mine.
13 And I do not want you to be unaware, brethren,
    that **often** I have planned to come to you
           (and have been prevented thus far)
    in order that I might obtain some FRUIT
        among YOU ALSO,
    even as among the rest of the Gentiles.
14 I AM UNDER OBLIGATION
    (1) both to Greeks and to barbarians,
    (2) both to the wise and to the foolish.
15 Thus, **for my part**,
    I AM EAGER TO PREACH THE GOSPEL
               to you also who are in Rome.

(margin: UNDER OBLIGATION)

16 FOR I am NOT ASHAMED
    of the GOSPEL,
    for it is the power (1) of God
                (2) for salvation
                (3) to everyone who believes,
                  to the Jew first
                  and also to the Greek.
17 For in it the righteousness of God
    is revealed from FAITH
           to FAITH;
    as it is written,
    "But the righteous man shall live by faith."
                      [Hab. 2:4]

(margin: UNASHAMED)

OBSERVATIONS

Key Words and Phrases

1:8 "faith" _____
  9 _____
 10 _____
 14 _____

16 _____
16 _____
17 _____
17 _____
others: _____

Segment Survey

Who is the segment mainly about? Note the opening phrase of each paragraph.

_____

_____

What feelings of Paul stand out in each paragraph? (Note the outline.) _____

_____

Which paragraph is mostly about the *message* of the gospel? _____

What references to the *whole world* do you see in the segment? Record these.

_____

_____

_____

Paragraph Analysis

1:8-10
1. What does Paul testify first (v. 8)?

_____

_____

2. How is this related to his prayer request (v.10)?

_____

_____

1:11-15
1. What reasons does Paul give for longing to see his friends? _____

_____

2. How does Paul identify himself as a debtor (v.14)? _____

_____

How does this bring Rome into the picture?

_____

_____

1:16-17
1. Recall from the survey study that these are key verses for Romans. Also, many words of the verses are key words of the letter. Record words that appear strong and closely related to what you learned is the theme of Romans.

_____

_____

2. Note how the gospel is identified with power (v. 16). To what else is it related (v. 17)?

_____

3. Who is mentioned as righteous: God, or a man, or both? _____

What is your definition of righteousness?

_____
_____

Related Verses

Acts 28:22 _____

Hab. 2:4 _____

Isa. 51:5, 6 _____

Gal. 3:11 _____

Rom. 8:2-4 _____

Acts 3:26 _____

Rom. 2:9, 10 _____

1. "Some spiritual gift" (1:11). (TBS#3) Who would "impart" the gift to the Romans?

Compare this with the giver of spiritual gifts mentioned in Romans 12:3-8.

_____

How does Romans 1:12 identify the spiritual gift of 1:11? _____

_____

2. "Salvation" (1:16). This is the first of 13 appearances of the word in Romans (including "saved" and "save"). Notice that Paul does not expand on the doctrine here. That will come later. But what requirement for salvation does he mention? _____

What word related to that requirement appears in verse 17? _____

Note that Paul has not yet explicitly used the words "faith" or "believe" with the *object* of that faith, Jesus Christ. That identification will come later. The doctrine of salvation is closely related to God's *righteousness*. What does Paul write about that righteousness in

verse 17? _____

3. In verse 17 Paul quotes Habakkuk's reference to "the righteous man." Compare this with Romans 3:10. Is this a contradiction? Explain.

_____

4. "From faith to faith" (1:17). The NIV paraphrases this, "by faith from first to last."

APPLICATIONS

1. What does this passage teach about your obligations to unsaved persons?

_____
_____

What can you do *today* to fulfill some of those? (TBS#7) _____

2. What do you learn here about your obligations to Christians who are babes in Christ?

_____

Summary of Passage

Paul thanks God for the spreading witness of the Roman Christians' faith, and he tells them how much he longs to see them and to minister to them.

The apostle has a deep conviction of his obligation to preach the gospel. He is not ashamed of the gospel, for it is God's power to save everyone who believes. It reveals how God's righteousness has a part in man's saving faith.

Memory Verses   1:16,17

Looking Ahead

Paul begins at the opening of the story of salvation by writing of the *need* for salvation: sinful man has incurred the wrath of God.

NEED OF
SALVATION
1:18–3:20

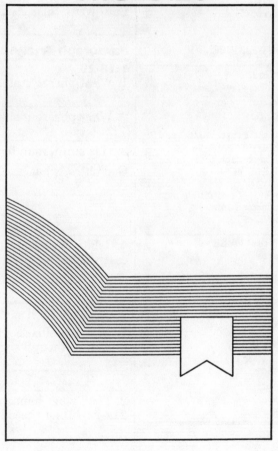

SETTING Paul has introduced the theme of his letter (1:1-17). Now he begins the story of salvation by describing the sin of man, which brings down God's wrath. Note on the survey chart that this is the first segment of the section called NEED OF SALVATION.

Book of Romans: GOD'S SALVATION FOR SINNER

P R O L O G U E	NEED OF SALVATION	WAY OF SALVATION	LIFE OF SALVATION	SCOPE OF SALVATION	SERVICES OF SALVATION	E P I L O G U E
		DOCTRINAL			PRACTICAL	
	GOD'S POWER	GOD'S GRACE	GOD'S HOLINESS	GOD'S SOVEREIGNTY	GOD'S GLORY	
1:1	1:18	3:21	6:1	9:1	12:1	15:1

Segment Survey

This is a segment of three paragraphs. Follow the outline shown on the textual re-creation chart, as you read the Bible text. Tell in your own words what each paragraph is about:

1:18-20 _____

1:21-23 _____

1:24-25 _____

Compare the first and last phrases of the

segment. _____

_____

What is the last word of the segment? Why did

Paul write this? _____

_____

WRATH OF GOD

18 For the WRATH OF GOD
　　is REVEALED from HEAVEN
　against
　　　(1) all ungodliness and
　　　(2) unrighteousness of men,
　　　　who suppress THE TRUTH
　　　　　in unrighteousness,
19 because that which is KNOWN about GOD
　　　　　　　is EVIDENT within them;
　　for God made it EVIDENT to them.
20 For since the creation of the world
　　(1) His invisible attributes,
　　(2) His eternal power and
　　(3) divine nature,
　　have been CLEARLY SEEN,
　　being UNDERSTOOD
　　　through what has been made,
　so that THEY ARE WITHOUT EXCUSE.

A REVEALED GOD

21 For even though they **knew God**,
　　they did not
　　　(1) **honor Him as God,**
　　　(2) or **give thanks**;
　　but
　　　(1) they became futile in their speculations, and
　　　(2) their **foolish heart** was **darkened**.
22　　(3) Professing to be wise, they became **fools**, and
23　　(4) exchanged the GLORY of the
　　　　INCORRUPTIBLE GOD
　　　　　for an image in the form of corruptible man
　　　　　and of birds and four-footed animals
　　　　　and crawling creatures.

CORRUPT MAN

24 THEREFORE GOD GAVE THEM OVER
　　　in the **lusts** of their **hearts**
　　　to IMPURITY,
　　that their **bodies** might be **dishonored** among them.
25　For they exchanged
　　　the **TRUTH OF GOD** for a **LIE**,
　and worshiped
　and served the **CREATURE**
　　rather than the CREATOR,
　　　who is blessed forever.
　　　Amen.

INEVITABLE JUDGMENT

Paragraph Analysis

1:18-20
1. What phrase states man's sin?
_____

2. What phrase identifies God's reaction?
_____

3. Has sinful man been shown any truth about

God? If so, what? _____

_____

_____

4. Relate the last phrase "without excuse" to the

earlier one "suppress the truth."

_____

_____

_____

1:21-23
1. What two sins does the rebellious heart commit, even though shown who God is (v. 21a)?

_____

2. Then what happens in that sinful heart (vv. 21a-23)? (List these by words or short phrases.)

_____

_____

_____

_____

3. What phrase in this paragraph describes God?

_____

1:24-25
1. What is the impact of the first word?

_____

OBSERVATIONS
Key Words and Phrases

1:18 "wrath of God" _____

　18 _____

　19 _____

　21 _____

　23 _____

　24 _____

　25 _____

others: _____

2. In what different ways is the pagan heart's sin described in verse 25?_____

_____

_____

_____

3. What divine judgment is given for this?

_____

_____

_____

_____

Related Verses

Acts 14:17_____

_____

Job 12:7-10_____

_____

Ps. 106:19-20_____

_____

Eph. 4:17-20_____

INTERPRETATIONS

1. Does God reveal truth about Himself to all mankind? If so, what kind of truth is that?

_____

_____

_____

In what ways does He reveal that kind of truth?_____

_____

_____

2. What does verse 21 reveal about the kind of response God wants that truth to bring?

_____

_____

_____

3. Why would a person not want to honor God as God or thank Him? _____

_____

_____

_____

4. Do the God-rejectors of verses 21-23,25 worship anything? If so, what?

_____

_____

_____

5. What words of the last paragraph teach that God does not **force** a human heart to worship Him?_____

_____

_____

APPLICATIONS

1. Why does a sinner need to honor God as God, if his heart is to be in the right attitude and spirit to receive the gospel of salvation? In answering this, recall what 1:16 and 17 teach about God and the gospel.

_____

_____

_____

_____

2. What are some of the first things you would want to talk about when witnessing to an atheist or agnostic? Discuss this with your group.
(TBS#7)_____

_____

_____

_____

_____

3. How is this passage an answer to those who charge God with unfairness in judging sinners who have never heard or read the Bible?

_____

_____

_____

_____

Summary of Passage

God's judgment of wrath falls upon all who suppress the truth that has been revealed to them. This is revelation about who He is. The rejectors do not honor Him as God or give Him thanks. So He gives them over to their idolatrous ways of worshiping and serving the creature rather than the Creator.

A Memory Verse   1:25

Looking Ahead

Paul cites all kinds of sins committed by those who do not acknowledge God as God.

SETTING The last verse of the preceding segment introduces this segment. Sinners "worshiped and served the creature rather than the Creator," so God gave them over to the sins they desired, which are listed in the present passage.

Book of Romans: GOD'S SALVATION FOR SINNER

P R O L O G U E	NEED OF SALVATION	WAY OF SALVATION	LIFE OF SALVATION	SCOPE OF SALVATION	SERVICES OF SALVATION	E P I L O G U E
		DOCTRINAL			PRACTICAL	
	GOD'S POWER	GOD'S GRACE	GOD'S HOLINESS	GOD'S SOVEREIGNTY	GOD'S GLORY	
1:1	1:18	3:21	6:1	9:1	12:1	15:14

GOD GAVE THEM OVER

SINS OF PASSION

26   For this reason
        GOD GAVE THEM OVER
            to **degrading** passions;
        for their women **exchanged** the natural function
                for that which is unnatural,
27 and in the **same way also**
    the men **abandoned** the natural function
                        of the woman
        and burned in their **desire** toward one another,
            men with men committing **indecent acts**
                and **receiving** in their own persons
                    the **due penalty**
                        of their **ERROR.**

ALL KINDS OF SINS

28 And just as they did not see fit
            to ACKNOWLEDGE GOD any longer,
        GOD GAVE THEM OVER
            to a **depraved** mind,
        to do those things which are **not proper,**
29 **being** filled with
        all unrighteousness, wickedness, greed, evil;
        full of envy, murder, strife, deceit, malice;
30 they are gossips, slanderers, haters of God,
        insolent, arrogant, boastful,
        inventors of evil, disobedient to parents,
31   without understanding, untrustworthy,
        unloving, unmerciful;

32 and, although THEY KNOW
        the ORDINANCE OF GOD,
        that those who practice such things
            are **worthy of death,**
        they not only **do** the same,
            but also give **hearty** approval
                to those who practice them.

OBSERVATIONS

Key Words and Phrases

1:26 "passions" _____
    26 _____
    27 _____
    28 _____
    29 _____
    30 _____
    31 _____
    32 _____
others: _____
_____
_____

Segment Survey

Read the passage. Then, in your own words, write its theme. _____

What phrase is repeated toward the beginning of each paragraph? _____

Compare the phrases following that repeated phrase. _____
_____
_____
_____

Paragraph Analysis

1:26-27
1. Who are the "them" of verse 26?
_____

2. What two words of verse 26 describe their sins?
_____
_____

3. What other words does Paul use to describe these sins of passion? _____
_____
_____

4. What does Paul say about judgment for the sins? _____
_____
_____

1:28-32
1. What basic sin is first identified (v. 28)?
_____

2. To what does God give these people over?
_____
_____
_____

3. How are *thinking* and *doing* related in verse 28b? _____
_____
_____

4. Study the list of sins in verses 29-31. Record these below, and look for *groups* of similar sins. For example, note the similarity of these: unrighteousness, wickedness, greed, evil.
_____
_____
_____
_____
_____

_____
_____
_____
_____
_____
_____

5. What knowledge do these sinners have, according to verse 32? _____
_____

6. What double sin do you see in verse 32?
_____
_____

Related Verses
Lev. 18:22 _____
_____

Lev. 20:13 _____
_____

1 Thess. 4:5 _____
_____

1 Cor. 6:9-10 _____
_____

2 Tim. 3:1-5 _____
_____

INTERPRETATIONS
1. "God gave them over" (1:26). What does this statement suggest as to God's ministry with these sinners *before* they were deeply entrenched in the idolatrous ways of 1:21-25?
_____
_____
_____
_____

2. What are your observations about the large variety of sins mentioned in verses 29-31?
_____
_____
_____

Does the list include every kind of sin? What do you think is Paul's purpose in citing such a variety of sins? _____
_____
_____
_____
_____

APPLICATIONS
1. All sins originate in the thoughts of the heart, but the sins vary in their acts. Go through the list of sins of this passage, and identify each one with the following categories:

thoughts only: _____
_____
_____

body: _____
_____
_____

another person involved: _____
_____
_____

relations with others
family: _____
_____
_____
_____
_____

others: _____
_____
_____
_____

2. Do you know anyone who is still an unbeliever, living in sin and in the rejection of God's light? Pray much for that person, and use every opportunity to present the gospel.

Summary of Passage
The sinner who refuses to acknowledge God, spurning the light He has given, will sink deeper and deeper in all kinds of sin, receiving just recompense from God. His life-style is degrading passion and a depraved mind, and God gives him over to both.

A Memory Verse   1:28

Looking Ahead
Paul exposes the sin of the self-righteous moralist.

SETTING The preceding passage exposed the degraded depths of sinners on the loose. Now Paul warns stubborn and unrepentant souls not to excuse their sins by judging sins of others.

Book of Romans: GOD'S SALVATION FOR SINNER

P R O L O G U E	NEED OF SALVATION	WAY OF SALVATION	LIFE OF SALVATION	SCOPE OF SALVATION	SERVICES OF SALVATION	E P I L O G U E
			DOCTRINAL		PRACTICAL	
	GOD'S POWER	GOD'S GRACE	GOD'S HOLINESS	GOD'S SOVEREIGNTY	GOD'S GLORY	
1:1	1:18	3:21	6:1	9:1	12:1	15:1

GOD'S RIGHTEOUS JUDGMENT

1 Therefore you are **without excuse,**
      every man of you
        who passes **JUDGMENT,**
    for in that you JUDGE one another,
    you CONDEMN yourself;
    for you who JUDGE **practice** the same things.
2 And we **know** that
    THE JUDGMENT OF GOD **rightly falls**
      upon those who **practice** such things.
3 And **do you suppose** this, O man,
      when you pass JUDGMENT
        upon those who **practice** such things
        and DO THE SAME YOURSELF,
      that you will **escape** the JUDGMENT OF GOD?
4 Or ⟶ do you think **lightly**
    of the riches of His
      (1) kindness and
      (2) forbearance and
      (3) patience,
    not knowing that
      the KINDNESS of GOD
        leads you to REPENTANCE?

MAN JUDGING OTHERS

5 But **because** of your
      (1) stubbornness and
      (2) unrepentant heart
    you are storing up WRATH FOR YOURSELF
      in the day of
      (1) wrath and
      (2) revelation
      of the RIGHTEOUS JUDGMENT OF GOD;
6 who will render to **every man**
          according to his DEEDS [Ps. 62:12]:
7 to those who by perseverance in DOING GOOD
    seek for
      (1) glory and
      (2) honor and
      (3) immortality,
    ETERNAL LIFE;
8   But
    to those who
      (1) are selfishly ambitious and
      (2) do NOT OBEY THE TRUTH,
          but obey unrighteousness,
    WRATH AND INDIGNATION.
9 There will be
    TRIBULATION and DISTRESS
      for every soul of man who DOES EVIL,
      (1) of the Jew first and
      (2) also of the Greek,
10 but GLORY and HONOR and PEACE
    to every man who DOES GOOD,
      (1) to the Jew first and
      (2) also to the Greek.
11 For there is NO PARTIALITY WITH GOD.

GOD JUDGING MAN

OBSERVATIONS

Key Words and Phrases

2:1 "judgment" _____

3 _____

4 _____

5 _____

6 _____

7 _____

8 _____

11 _____

others: _____

Segment Survey

This segment is divided into two paragraphs. Whose judging is prominent in the first paragraph? _____

In the second? _____

How does the first paragraph open with a reference to sinners? _____

_____

How does it close with a reference to God?

_____

_____

Do the same comparative study in the second paragraph. _____

_____

Paragraph Analysis

2:1-4

1. What is the key repeated word of the paragraph? _____

2. In verse 1, who condemns the one who judges others? _____

3. Who is his condemner, according to verse 3? _____

4. According to verse 3, what is a motive of those who judge others but practice the things themselves? _____

_____

5. Observe that each of verses 3 and 4 is a question. Which one is a warning, and which is a rebuke? _____

_____

6. According to verse 4, what one word describes the spiritual responsibility of all sinners?

_____

7. How does God help in that need?

_____

2:5-11

1. Verse 5 is a transition verse. How do the first lines refer to the previous paragraph?

How do its last lines refer to the remainder of the segment?_____

2. In what two ways is God's judgment identified (v. 5 and v. 11)?
_____
_____

3. The remainder of the paragraph shows God at work as judge. Record the descriptions of the two ways and two judgments.

DEEDS	JUDGMENTS

Related Verses

Eph. 2:8-9 _____
_____

Matt. 7:1 ff. _____
_____

Rom. 9:23, 24 _____
_____

2 Peter 3:9 _____
_____

Heb. 10:36 _____
_____

Matt. 25:46 _____
_____

Acts 3:26 _____
_____

1 Peter 4:17 _____
_____

Rev. 20:11-12 _____

INTERPRETATIONS

1. "Every man of you" (2:1). The last time Paul addressed his readers as "you" was in 1:15. From 1:18 to 1:32 it was always "they," referring to "men who suppress the truth" (1:18). Now Paul returns to "you." What message in this segment, if any, is to believers as well as to unbelievers?
_____

2. Read Ephesians 2:8,9. Observe that salvation is not of works. Then read Romans 2:6-7. Does God give eternal life for good deeds or for the acceptable *heart which brings forth those deeds?*

How is your answer supported by the teaching of verses 8-10?_____

3. "Jew first and...Greek" (2:9-10). Impartial recompense is for *all*: Jew and non-Jew (Greek). The priority word, "first," is one of accountability, not time. The Jews had the light of written revelation, and so were held more accountable.

APPLICATIONS

1. What do you learn here about judging other people's actions and motives?
_____
_____

2. In what ways should fear of just recompense for one's actions be a deterrent to evil?
_____
_____

3. What do you learn about God's view of the *deeds* of men?_____

4. What traits and qualities of living that are pleasing to God do you see in this passage? Record them. Are you weak in any of those areas? If so, think about how you can get victory, and do it. _____

Summary of Passage

No one, in a self-righteous spirit, can hide his own sins by judging the sins of others. The unrepentant heart rejects the redemptive work of God's kindness and will reap the righteous judgment of God. Eternal life is for the one whose deeds come from a righteous and obedient heart. God's wrath is for the unrepentant soul who does evil.

A Memory Verse   2:4

Looking Ahead

Paul will show why Gentiles will be judged on judgment day by the gospel of Jesus Christ.

SETTING This passage brings Paul's discussion about judgment for self-righteous moralists up to the last judgment "through Christ Jesus" (2:16).

Book of Romans: GOD'S SALVATION FOR SINNERS

P R O L O G U E	NEED OF SALVATION	WAY OF SALVATION	LIFE OF SALVATION	SCOPE OF SALVATION	SERVICES OF SALVATION	E P I L O G U E
		DOCTRINAL			PRACTICAL	16: 27
	GOD'S POWER	GOD'S GRACE	GOD'S HOLINESS	GOD'S SOVEREIGNTY	GOD'S GLORY	
1:1	1:18	3:21	6:1	9:1	12:1	15:14

WHO WILL BE JUSTIFIED?

12 FOR all who have SINNED **without the Law**
    will also PERISH **without the Law**;
  and all who have SINNED **under the Law**
    will be JUDGED by the Law;
13 For not the HEARERS of the Law
    are **just** before God,
  but the DOERS of the Law
    will be **justified**.

JUDGMENT FOR SIN

14 [For when Gentiles
        who do not have the Law
  do instinctively
       the **things of the Law,**
  these, not having the Law,
    are a Law to themselves,
15 in that
  they **show** the WORK of the Law
    written IN THEIR HEARTS,
  THEIR CONSCIENCE bearing **witness,**
  and **THEIR THOUGHTS**
    alternately accusing
      or else defending them,]
16 on the day when,
    according to my GOSPEL,
GOD WILL JUDGE
  the secrets of men
THROUGH CHRIST JESUS.

JUDGMENT THROUGH CHRIST

OBSERVATIONS

Key Words and Phrases

2:12 "without the Law"_____

  12_____

  13_____

  13_____

  14_____

  15_____

  16_____

  16_____

others:_____

Segment Survey

The key repeated word throughout the segment is "Law." Mark with a pencil every reference to it in the textual re-creation.

The first paragraph shows what the Law has to do with God's declaring a man righteous. The concluding reference in the second paragraph is to the event ("on the day") when God will so judge.

Note: verses 14 and 15 may be read as parenthetical. Try reading the other verses in this order: 12, 13, 16.

Paragraph Analysis

2:12-13

1. The paragraph has two groups of two statements each. Observe these.
2. What are the four phrases about "Law" in these comparisons?

v. 12 _____the Law

_____ the Law

v. 13 _____ of the Law

_____ of the Law

3. Gentiles are those "without the Law." (See v. 14a.) What is the judgment for their sin?

_____

_____

4. Jews are those "under the Law." What judges their sin? _____

_____

Paul's main point of verse 12 is, "God will punish sin *wherever* it is found."

5. Who will be justified (declared "just" or "righteous") before God? _____

Compare this with your earlier study of 2:6-10.

2:14-16

1. There are people who do not know of, or have, a Bible. Does this mean they have no "law" or instruction telling them what is right and what is wrong? How does Paul answer this question in these verses? _____

_____

_____

_____

2. What three words refer to the spirit of man?

_____

_____

3. What does verse 16 teach about these truths:

the Judge:_____

objects of judgment:_____

standard of judgment:_____

Related Verses

Rom. 9:4 _____

_____

Acts 4:12_____

_____

Rom. 10:4_____

1 Cor. 9:19-21 _____

Matt. 7:21 _____

Acts 10:35 _____

INTERPRETATIONS

1. When Paul wrote Romans, there was only the Old Testament, known as the Law. Paul referred to Gentiles (non-Jews) as those who did not have the written Scriptures: they were "without the Law" (2:12). But they did have a natural law: God's voice speaking to their inner spirit through their conscience and thought-life. Recall also the natural revelation of 1:20.

2. Regardless of what law he has, in the end a man is justified not for being a hearer but for practicing the Law out of a heart pleasing to God.

3. This is the first appearance of the words "just" and "justified" in the epistle. Definition: Justification is the judicial act of God in declaring a sinner righteous. (The words "righteous" and "righteousness" first appeared at 1:17.) Later in the epistle Paul will show that salvation is being declared righteous, that is, being justified.

4. What do you think Paul means by the phrase "through Christ Jesus" in verse 16?

_____
_____
_____
_____
_____
_____

APPLICATIONS

1. Why is it easy or difficult to *practice* consistently what we know to be right?

_____
_____
_____

2. In what way are deeds a measure of the heart?

_____
_____
_____
_____
_____

Who alone knows fully the heart behind the deed? How does that secure the justice of the last judgment? _____

_____

3. How can you use this passage in witnessing to an unsaved person? _____

_____
_____
_____
_____
_____
_____

Summary of Passage

When God judges the secrets of men through Christ Jesus, the judgment is based on what they do with the law they have, written or unwritten.

A Memory Verse   2:13

Looking Ahead

Paul will show that the non-believing Jew is also a condemned sinner despite the fact that he is very religious.

SETTING Paul continues the theme of condemnation of sinners. In 1:18-32 he showed the pagan world condemned; in 2:1-16, the self-righteous condemned. Now he begins to show the Jew's condemnation (units 7 and 8); and in 3:9-20 the whole world is seen as guilty.

Book of Romans: GOD'S SALVATION FOR SINNER

P R O L O G U E	NEED OF SALVATION	WAY OF SALVATION	LIFE OF SALVATION	SCOPE OF SALVATION	SERVICES OF SALVATION	E P I L O G U E
		DOCTRINAL			PRACTICAL	
	GOD'S POWER	GOD'S GRACE	GOD'S HOLINESS	GOD'S SOVEREIGNTY	GOD'S GLORY	
1:1	1:18	3:21	6:1	9:1	12:1	15:1

22 _____

23 _____

24 _____

25 _____

29 _____

others: _____

WHAT IS A JEW?

HYPOCRITICAL JEW

17 BUT if you
   bear the **name** JEW, and **rely** upon the LAW, and
18 **boast** in GOD, and **know** HIS WILL, and
   approve the things that are essential,
      being **instructed** out of the LAW, and
19 are confident **that you yourself are**
      (1) a GUIDE to the **blind**,
      (2) a LIGHT to those who are in **darkness**,
20   (3) a CORRECTOR of the **foolish**,
      (4) a TEACHER of the immature,
   having in the LAW
   the embodiment of KNOWLEDGE and of the TRUTH,
21 you, THEREFORE, who **TEACH** another,
      do you not TEACH YOURSELF?
      You who **PREACH** that one should not steal,
      do you steal?
22 You who **SAY** that one should not commit adultery,
      do you commit adultery?
   You who **ABHOR** idols,
      do you rob temples?
23 You who **BOAST** in the LAW,
      through your breaking the LAW,
      do you dishonor God?
24 For "the NAME OF GOD
      is BLASPHEMED among the Gentiles
         because of you,"
      just as it is written. [Isa. 52:5, Ezek. 36:20 ff.]

THE TEST

25 For indeed
      circumcision is of value,
         if you PRACTICE THE LAW;
         BUT if you are a TRANSGRESSOR of THE LAW,
      your circumcision has become uncircumcision.
26 If therefore
   the uncircumcised man
         KEEPS the requirements of the LAW,
   will not his uncircumcision
      be regarded as circumcision?
27 And will not he who is physically uncircumcised,
      if he KEEPS THE LAW,
   will he not judge YOU
         WHO though having the letter of the LAW
                           and circumcision
      ARE a TRANSGRESSOR OF THE LAW?

TRUE JEW

28 For he is not a JEW who is one OUTWARDLY;
   neither is circumcision that which is
                     OUTWARD IN THE FLESH.
29 But HE IS A JEW who is one INWARDLY;
   and circumcision is that which is
      OF THE HEART,
      BY THE SPIRIT,
      not by the letter;
   and **his** praise is not from men,
      but FROM GOD.

OBSERVATIONS

Key Words and Phrases

2:17 "the name Jew"

18 _____

21 _____

Segment Survey

The segment is of three paragraphs. Who is the subject of all three? _____
(Note: In the epistle a circumcised man is a Jew, and an uncircumcised man is a Gentile. This is because the rite of circumcision was part of the Jews' religion in the early days. See Genesis 17:1-11.)

What kind of Jew does Paul describe in the first paragraph? _____
_____
_____

What kind of Jew does he describe in the last paragraph? _____
_____
_____

What does the middle paragraph contribute to the segment? _____
_____
_____

Paragraph Analysis

2:17-24

1. Make a list of the good things said about a Jew in verses 17-20: _____
_____
_____
_____

2. What does Paul expose about some Jews, in verses 21-23? _____
_____

3. In what strong way does he label the sin, in verse 24? _____
_____

2:25-27

1. What is the key repeated three-letter word of this paragraph? _____
How is it a test of a true Jew?
_____
_____

2. What does Paul say about a Gentile who keeps the Law (v. 27)?_____
_____
_____

2:28-29
List Paul's various descriptions of a true Jew:
_____
_____
_____
_____

Related Verses

Gen. 17:10 ff._____
_____

Deut. 30:6_____
_____

Jer. 9:25, 26_____
_____

Gal. 5:3_____
_____

Acts 7:51_____
_____

Phil. 3:2-6_____
_____

Ezek. 44:7_____
_____

INTERPRETATIONS

1. "Jew" (2:17). The three titles, "Jew," "Hebrew" and "Israelite" refer to the same people. "Jew" (first reference, 2 Kings 16:6) identifies them as a race distinct from Gentiles. "Hebrew" (first reference, Genesis 14:13) implies origin and language. "Israelite" (first reference, Genesis 32:28) brings out their relation to God (yisra-el, 'God strives').

2. In verses 21-23 do you think Paul is charging that his readers were guilty of all those sins? If not, what was he saying?
_____
_____
_____
_____

3. What does verse 24 mean?
_____
_____
_____
_____
_____

4. "Circumcision" (2:25). When God made a covenant between Himself and Abraham and his descendants, He ordained physical circumcision as a sign of that covenant (Gen. 17:10). The covenant was a spiritual relationship between God and Israel, so the people's heart to obey the Law was the measure of true relationship. In your own words, what is the difference between flesh circumcision and heart circumcision?
_____
_____
_____
_____
_____
_____

APPLICATIONS

1. The Jews were blessed with privileges and opportunities to minister to other people, but they failed to keep their own hearts right before God. How does this temptation affect Christian work today?_____
_____
_____
_____

What can a Christian worker do to help him watch his *own* heart, as he ministers to others?
_____
_____
_____

2. Paul compares *praise from God* with *praise from men*. What are the dangers of praise from men?
_____
_____
_____
_____

What kind of praise from God do you value?
_____
_____
_____

Summary of Passage

A Jew has many privileges and opportunities for service to others, but he blasphemes God's name when he acts like a hypocrite.

To be a true Jew, a man needs to practice the Law from the heart, by the aid of the Spirit. For this, God praises him.

A Memory Verse 2:29

Looking Ahead

Paul will show that even the unbelieving hearts of some Jews will not take away from the faithfulness of God.

SETTING Earlier (2:17-29), Paul showed that unbelieving Jews are judged by their inconsistent testimony and non-practice of the Law. Now he sharpens his indictment by describing the unchanging character of God, whose judgments do not abate when the Jews' sins increase.

Book of Romans: GOD'S SALVATION FOR SINNERS

P R O L O G U E	NEED OF SALVATION	WAY OF SALVATION	LIFE OF SALVATION	SCOPE OF SALVATION	SERVICES OF SALVATION	E P I L O G U E
			DOCTRINAL		PRACTICAL	
	GOD'S POWER	GOD'S GRACE	GOD'S HOLINESS	GOD'S SOVEREIGNTY	GOD'S GLORY	
1:1	1:18	3:21	6:1	9:1	12:1	15:14

THE UNCHANGING GOD

1 Then WHAT ADVANTAGE has THE JEW?
Or WHAT is the BENEFIT of circumcision?
GREAT in **every** respect.
First of all,
that they were **entrusted** with the ORACLES of God.
2 What then?
If some did not **believe**,
their unbelief will not nullify
the FAITHFULNESS of GOD,
will it?
4 May it never be!
Rather, let GOD be found TRUE,
though **every man** be found a LIAR,
as it is written,
"that thou mightest be JUSTIFIED in THY WORDS,
and mightest PREVAIL when thou [dost judge]."
[Ps. 51:4]

FAITHFUL SPEAKER

5 But if **our unrighteousness**
demonstrates the RIGHTEOUSNESS OF GOD,
what shall we say?
The God who inflicts WRATH
is **not unrighteous**, is He?
(I am speaking in human terms.)
6 May it never be!
For otherwise HOW will GOD JUDGE THE WORLD?
7 But if through **my lie**
the TRUTH OF GOD ABOUNDED TO HIS GLORY,
why am I also still being JUDGED
as a SINNER?
8 And why not say
(as we are slanderously reported
and as some affirm that we say),
"Let us DO EVIL that GOOD MAY COME"?
Their CONDEMNATION is JUST.

JUST JUDGE

OBSERVATIONS

Key Words and Phrases

3:1 "what advantage?" _____

2 _____

3 _____

4 _____

5 _____

6 _____

7 _____

8 _____

others: _____

_____

Segment Survey

The segment opens with a question which suggests that the whole passage is about the favored position of the Jew. Read the passage, and see if this is so.

Actually, Paul writes mostly about God. Read the passage again, and observe things he says. For example, justify the outline shown:

FAITHFUL SPEAKER
JUST JUDGE

As the gulf widens between the unchanging God and the changing Jews, how does this sharpen the indictment against the Jews?

_____
_____

_____

How is the last sentence of the passage a fitting conclusion?_____

_____

_____

Paragraph Analysis

3:1-4
1. What is Paul's answer to the opening question?
_____

_____

His words "First of all" suggest a multi-fold answer. See if you can find any other answers in the whole segment.
2. What different things does Paul say about this oracle-speaking God?_____

_____

_____

3. How does he contrast that God with some Jews? _____

_____

_____

4. What does this add to the indictment against the Jews?_____

_____

_____

3:5-8
1. Note the statement "I am speaking in human terms" (v. 5). Read each of the following verses as human arguments of hecklers probing and testing God's character. Write them in your own words:

v. 5:_____

_____

_____

(Note Paul's answer: verse 6.)

verse 7:_____

_____

_____

verse 8a:_____

_____

_____

(Note Paul's reaction: verse 8b.)
2. How does this emphasize the just character of
God as judge? _____

_____

Related Verses

Deut. 4:8_____

_____

Ps. 147:19_____

_____

Rom. 6:1 ff. _____

_____

Rom. 9:4, 5_____

_____

Rom. 10:16_____

_____

Acts 7:38_____

_____

INTERPRETATIONS

1. "First of all" (3:2). Paul's answer to his opening
question suggests more answers to come, but
they do not appear in this passage. See 9:4-5 for
other answers which he may have had in mind.
2. Why was it an advantage to the Jews to be
entrusted with oracles of God, such as commandments, promises and prophecies?

_____

_____

_____

3. In what different ways does this passage show
God to be *absolutely* just—that is, not variable
and relative to the sinfulness of man?

_____

_____

_____

4. Verse 7 is not Paul's argument, but that of
the debaters (as in verse 5). The NIV prints the
verse in quotes, and adds the introductory words,
"Someone might argue."
5. What does the last sentence of verse 8 mean,
and to whom does it refer?

_____

_____

_____

APPLICATIONS

1. In what ways are you advantaged to have the
Bible, God's Word to you?

_____

_____

_____

_____

2. Does this advantage make you more accountable than those who do not even know that a
Bible exists? If so, how? What are you doing to
show God your gratitude for His Word? What

more can you do?_____

_____

_____

_____

_____

_____

Summary of Passage

The Jew has great advantage in having the
Scriptures. However, unbelievers are guilty for
their rejection of God and His Word, and are
judged as sinners. God's righteousness and
goodness remain the same, even though He must
bring judgment upon the very ones whom He
entrusted with His oracles. The condemnation of
unbelieving Jews is deserved.

Memory Verses 3:1,2

Looking Ahead

Paul will conclude the section on the NEED OF
SALVATION (1:18–3:20) by concluding that
everyone is a sinner.

SETTING This is the conclusion of the section NEED OF SALVATION (1:18–3:20). Paul has shown these to be condemned as sinners: pagan world (1:18-32); self-righteous (2:1-16); and Jewish religionists (2:17–3:8). Now he summarizes by Scripture that *everyone* is a sinner in need of salvation.

Book of Romans: GOD'S SALVATION FOR SINNER

P R O L O G U E	NEED OF SALVATION	WAY OF SALVATION	LIFE OF SALVATION	SCOPE OF SALVATION	SERVICES OF SALVATION	E P I L O G U E
		DOCTRINAL			PRACTICAL	
	GOD'S POWER	GOD'S GRACE	GOD'S HOLINESS	GOD'S SOVEREIGNTY	GOD'S GLORY	
1:1	1:18	3:21	6:1	9:1	12:1	15:1

ALL ARE SINNERS

9 What then?
    Are we BETTER than they?
        Not at all;
    for we have already **charged**
        that BOTH JEWS and GREEKS
        are ALL UNDER SIN;
10 as it is written,   [Ps. 14:1-3, Ps. 53:1-4]
    "There is none RIGHTEOUS, NOT EVEN ONE;
11 There is none who UNDERSTANDS,
    There is none who SEEKS FOR GOD;
12   ALL have **turned aside**,
        together they have become **useless**;
    There is none who DOES GOOD,
    There is NOT EVEN ONE."

NO ONE RIGHTEOUS

13 "Their THROAT is an **open grave**, [Ps. 5:9, Ps. 140:3]
    With their TONGUES they **keep deceiving**,"
    "The poison of asps is under their LIPS";
14 "Whose MOUTH is full of cursing and bitterness";
15 "Their FEET are swift to shed blood,
            [Ps. 10:7, Isa. 59:7 ff]
16   "Destruction and misery are in their paths,
    and the path of peace
        have they not known."
18 "There is NO FEAR OF GOD
        before their EYES." [Ps. 36:1]

SINFUL LIVING

19 Now we know
    that **whatever** THE LAW SAYS,
    it speaks to those
        who are UNDER THE LAW,
    THAT EVERY MOUTH MAY BE CLOSED,
    and ALL THE WORLD
        may become ACCOUNTABLE TO GOD;
20 because
    by the WORKS of the LAW
        no flesh will be JUSTIFIED in His sight;
    for through the LAW comes the KNOWLEDGE of SIN.

LAW CONDEMNS

OBSERVATIONS

Key Words and Phrases

3:9   "all under sin" _____

  10 _____

  13 _____

  17 _____

  18 _____

  19 _____

  19 _____

  20 _____

others: _____

_____

Segment Survey

Observe that most of the segment is made up of Old Testament quotes. There are three paragraphs, each centered on the main subject of universal sin. Note what is said about sin in the opening verse and the concluding one.

Record with a phrase what each paragraph says about these subjects:

3:9-12 SINNERS_____

3:13-18 SINNING _____

3:19-20 LAW _____

How does this segment conclude the section 1:18–3:20?_____

_____

_____

Paragraph Analysis

(Read the Old Testament sources shown with the textual re-creation.)

3:9-12

1. In verse 9a, who are the "we" and the "they"? To answer this, keep in mind the preceding section (3:1-8) and the phrase "Jews and Greeks" in verse 9b. _____

_____

2. In what different ways are sinners identified in verses 10-12?_____

_____

_____

_____

Which identification relates them to God?

_____

3:13-18

1. What descriptions are about speech?

_____

2. What areas of one's living are described in verses 15-17?_____

_____

3. What part of the body is mentioned by verse 18?_____

_____

3:19-20

1. According to these verses, what does the law of God do for man: save him, or show him that he cannot keep the law because he is sinful?

_____

What phrases of the text support your answer?

_____

2. Compare verse 20 with this *Living Bible* paraphrase: "No one can ever be made right in God's sight by doing what the law commands. For the more we know of God's laws, the clearer it becomes that we aren't obeying them; His laws serve only to make us see that we are sinners."

Related Verses

Ps. 143:2_____

_____

Gal. 2:16_____

_____

James 2:10_____

_____

Rom. 7:7 _____

_____

Gal. 3:24_____

_____

Acts 13:38,39_____

_____

INTERPRETATIONS

1. "All under sin" (3:9). This may be interpreted as all under the power and control of sin.
2. "There is none who does good" (3:12). In this paragraph Paul is not denying that a person can and does perform good deeds. He is teaching that everyone born into this world is by nature a sinner, not righteous, and that everyone sins. James writes that "whoever keeps the whole law and yet stumbles in one point, he has become guilty of all" (James 2:10).
3. What kind of sin do you think is meant by 3:18?

_____

_____

_____

4. According to verse 19, what must everyone recognize and confess before God?

_____

_____

5. Why is it important to offer a person the *knowledge* that he is a sinner?

_____

_____

_____

APPLICATIONS

In your witnessing to the unsaved, it is necessary to show the person his *need* of salvation, that he is a sinner. Read this passage again, and record a list of its teachings which you would want to share with him during the course of your witness.

(TBS#7)_____

_____

_____

_____

_____

_____

_____

_____

_____

_____

_____

Summary of Passage

Everyone has sinned (3:9-12); their sin has totally defiled their spirit (3:13-18); and the final verdict is "guilty before God" (3:19). The Law cannot help them because its very purpose is to reveal sin, not to relieve it.

Memory Verses   3:10,11

Looking Ahead

Paul will show where sinful man can find spiritual help.

WAY OF SALVATION
3:21–5:21

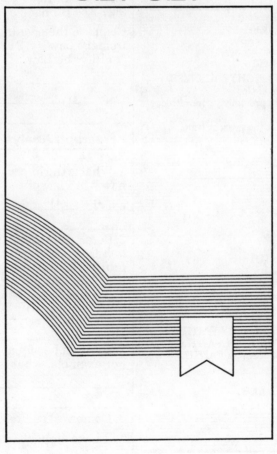

SETTING Note on the survey chart that this segment begins the second doctrinal section of the epistle, WAY OF SALVATION. Paul has shown that everyone needs salvation. Now he will show the sinner how to be saved.

Book of Romans: GOD'S SALVATION FOR SINNERS

P R O L O G U E	NEED OF SALVATION	WAY OF SALVATION	LIFE OF SALVATION	SCOPE OF SALVATION	SERVICES OF SALVATION	E P I L O G U E 16 27
		DOCTRINAL			PRACTICAL	
	GOD'S POWER	GOD'S GRACE	GOD'S HOLINESS	GOD'S SOVEREIGNTY	GOD'S GLORY	
1:1	1:18	3:21	6:1	9:1	12:1	15:14

HOW TO BE JUSTIFIED

21 But now apart from the LAW
   the RIGHTEOUSNESS of GOD has been manifested,
      being witnessed by the LAW and the PROPHETS;
22 even
   (1) the RIGHTEOUSNESS of GOD
   (2) through FAITH in Jesus Christ
   (3) for ALL those who BELIEVE;
      for there is no distinction;
23 for ALL HAVE SINNED
   and FALL SHORT of the Glory of God,
24 being JUSTIFIED
   (1) as a **gift**
   (2) by His **grace**
   (3) through the **redemption**
   which is in Christ Jesus

RIGHTEOUSNESS OF GOD

25   whom
         God displayed publicly
         as a propitiation
         in His blood
         through faith.
   This was to demonstrate HIS RIGHTEOUSNESS,
      because in the forbearance of God
         He passed over the SINS previously committed;
26 for the demonstration, I say,
   of HIS RIGHTEOUSNESS at the present time,
that He might be just
   and the justifier
      of the one who has FAITH IN JESUS.

BLOOD OF CHRIST

27 Where then is boasting?
            It is excluded.
   By what kind of law?
            Of works?
   No, but by A LAW OF FAITH.
   28 For we maintain that
   a man is JUSTIFIED BY FAITH
      apart from works of the LAW.
29 Or is God the **God of Jews only**?
   Is He not the **God of Gentiles also**?
                     YES, of Gentiles also
30   —since indeed GOD
   who will JUSTIFY the circumcised BY FAITH
      and the uncircumcised THROUGH FAITH is one.
31 Do we **then nullify** the LAW through FAITH?
   May it never be!
      On the contrary,
         WE ESTABLISH THE LAW.

LAW OF FAITH

OBSERVATIONS

Key Words and Phrases

3:21 "righteousness of God" _____
 22 _____
 23 _____
 24 _____
 24 _____
 25 _____
 27 _____

 28 _____
others: _____

Segment Survey

The segment may be divided into three paragraphs. Observe in the textual re-creation how the first paragraph leads into the second: CHRIST JESUS ▶ whom.

Read each paragraph, and observe what is emphasized in each. Compare your observations with these:

3:21-24   God's righteousness
3:25-26   Christ's public sacrifice
3:27-31   Sinner's approach by faith

Compare the opening reference to Law, "apart from the Law" (v. 21), with the closing reference, "nullify the Law...?" (v. 31).

_____
_____
_____

Paragraph Analysis

3:21-24
1. What is the impact of the opening words, "But now," in view of the preceding section of the epistle? _____
_____

2. Recall from an earlier study that in *justification* God *declares* a sinner *righteous* when he fulfills God's requirements. Note the word "justified" in this paragraph. What does Paul say about the God side of justification (vv. 21,24)?

_____
_____

What does he say about the man side (v. 22)? For example, what is the way to justification?

_____
_____

3. Compare "righteousness of God" (3:21) and "all have sinned" (3:23). _____
_____
_____

What does this tell you about justification?

_____
_____
_____
_____
_____

3:25-26

1. Jesus died for the sins of the whole world. What verse tells of His death?

_____

2. What parts of this passage teach that Jesus died for sins committed before His time, and while Paul was writing? _____

_____

3. Jesus is justifier of whom (3:26)?

_____

_____

3:27-31

1. What is the key repeated word of the paragraph? _____

2. How are faith and Law compared in verse 28?

_____

_____

Related Verses

Rom. 5:1,9 _____

_____

1 Cor. 6:11 _____

_____

1 Tim. 3:16 _____

_____

Titus 3:7 _____

_____

Rev. 5:9 _____

_____

Heb. 2:17 _____

_____

INTERPRETATIONS

1. In justification, God declares the sinner righteous, in Christ. Christ's righteousness is imputed to him. In redemption (3:24), Christ offers His life as a ransom, to give deliverance from the bondage of Satan and sin, and to release to a new relationship to God. Propitiation (3:25, NIV) is God's presenting Jesus as a sacrifice of atonement, to demonstrate His justice in justifying sinners.

2. How were sinners of Old Testament times saved? For example, what about Abraham? Read Galatians 3:6. Compare this with what Paul teaches about justification in this Romans passage. _____

_____

_____

_____

_____

_____

3. The question "By what kind of law" (3:27) may be read as "On what principle?" (NIV). Also, the statement, "we establish the Law" (3:31) may be read "we uphold the Law" (NIV).

APPLICATIONS

1. In the last unit we studied that portion of Romans which establishes the sinner's need for salvation. When you are witnessing to an unsaved person, you will next want to show him the way of salvation, which is faith. Which truths of this passage would you want to share at this time? (TBS#7) _____

_____

_____

_____

_____

_____

_____

2. The salvation offered by God in Christ is a free gift. How does Paul emphasize this in the two phrases "as a gift by His grace" (3:24)?

_____

_____

_____

_____

Summary of Passage

All have sinned, but God has made a way of salvation by giving His Son to die for those sins. All who believe in Him are declared righteous. This justification is all of grace, apart from the works of the Law.

Memory Verses   3:23,24

Looking Ahead

Paul will illustrate the doctrine of justification by describing the experience of Abraham.

SETTING Paul has just written that "a man is justified by faith apart from works of the Law" (3:28). Now he will illustrate this in the life of Abraham, who lived before the Law was given.

Book of Romans: GOD'S SALVATION FOR SINNER

P R O L O G U E	NEED OF SALVATION	WAY OF SALVATION	LIFE OF SALVATION	SCOPE OF SALVATION	SERVICES OF SALVATION	E P I L O G U E
			DOCTRINAL		PRACTICAL	
	GOD'S POWER	GOD'S GRACE	GOD'S HOLINESS	GOD'S SOVEREIGNTY	GOD'S GLORY	
1:1	1:18	3:21	6:1	9:1	12:1	15:1

FAITH RECKONED AS RIGHTEOUSNESS

1 WHAT then shall we say that
   ABRAHAM, our forefather according to the flesh,
   HAS FOUND?
2 For if Abraham was JUSTIFIED BY WORKS,
   he has something to boast about;
     but **not before God.**
3 For what does the Scripture say?
   "And ABRAHAM BELIEVED GOD,   [Gen. 15:6]
      and IT
   was **reckoned** to him as RIGHTEOUSNESS."
4 Now to the one who **works,**
   his wage is not reckoned as a favor,
     but as what is due.
5 But to the one who does **not** work,
   but BELIEVES IN HIM
     who JUSTIFIES the ungodly,
   HIS FAITH is reckoned as RIGHTEOUSNESS.
6 Just as DAVID ALSO
   speaks of the blessing upon the man
   to whom God reckons RIGHTEOUSNESS
       apart from works:
7 "Blessed are those
     whose **lawless deeds** HAVE BEEN FORGIVEN,
   and whose **sins** HAVE BEEN COVERED. [Ps. 32:1
8 "Blessed is the man
   whose SIN the Lord will not TAKE INTO ACCOUNT."
          [Ps. 32:2

(right margin: NOT BY WORKS)

9 Is this BLESSING then upon the circumcised,
        or upon the uncircumcised also?
   For we say,
   "FAITH was RECKONED to ABRAHAM
     as RIGHTEOUSNESS."
10 HOW then was it reckoned?
     While he was circumcised, or uncircumcised?
   NOT while circumcised, **BUT** while uncircumcised;
11   and he received
   the **SIGN** of circumcision,
   a **SEAL** of the RIGHTEOUSNESS of the FAITH
     which he had while uncircumcised,
   that he might be
     (1) the FATHER of ALL WHO BELIEVE
            without being circumcised,
   that RIGHTEOUSNESS might be **reckoned to them,**
12 and
     (2) the FATHER of circumcision
      to those who not only are of the circumcision,
      but who **also** follow in the steps
        of **our father Abraham**
        which he had while uncircumcised.

(right margin: NOT BY RITE)

13 For the promise to Abraham or to his descendants
     that he would be **HEIR OF THE WORLD**
   was **NOT** through **THE LAW,**
     BUT through the RIGHTEOUSNESS
      of FAITH.
14. For **if** those who are of the **LAW** are HEIRS,
       FAITH is made **void**
     and THE PROMISE is **nullified;**
15 For the LAW brings about **WRATH,**
   but where there is **no** law,
         neither is there **violation.**

(right margin: NOT BY LAW)

OBSERVATIONS

Key Words and Phrases

4:1 "Abraham"_____

2 _____

3 _____

3 _____

6 _____

7 _____

9 _____

13 _____

others: _____

Segment Survey

First read the segment. Who is the central person of all three paragraphs? Does Christ appear by any of His names in the passage?

Notice the title given on the textual re-creation chart. Mark on your copy every appearance of the word "reckon(ed)," including the pharase where it appears.

In the first section of the epistle (1:18–3:20) Paul had shown that everyone is guilty as sinners. Look for the word "sin" (and synonyms) in this passage.

Observe the phrases of each paragraph that support this outline:

     4:1-8 NOT BY WORKS
     4:9-12 NOT BY RITE
     4:13-15 NOT BY LAW

Paragraph Analysis

4:1-8

1. What was reckoned to Abraham as righteousness?_____

In your own words, how does this describe his relationship to God? _____

2. What does Paul write about *works* in this paragraph?_____

3. In what three ways does David speak of God's dealing with the sin problem?

_____

_____

4:9-12

1. Recall from your earlier studies who "the circumcision" and "the uncircumcised" are.

2. The historical record of Abraham's circumcision at age 99 is reported in Genesis 17:24. Did God reckon Abraham as righteous *before* he was circumcised? (Compare Romans 4:10 with Genesis 15:6.) If so, what was the purpose of his being circumcised? _____

_____

In what sense is Abraham the father of Jews *and* the father of Gentiles? _____

_____

4:13-15

What was God's basis for promising Abraham that he would be heir of the world? (Cf. Gen. 17:1-8.) _____

_____

Related Verses

Gen. 15:6 _____

_____

Gen. 17:24 _____

_____

James 2:21-24 _____

_____

Rom. 9:8 _____

_____

Gal. 3:8,16,18 _____

_____

Heb. 11:8 _____

_____

2 Peter 1:1 _____

INTERPRETATIONS

1. "It was reckoned to him as righteousness" (4:3). Abraham was accounted, or regarded, as righteous. What kind of righteousness is this? What is the key to its being fully sufficient for the salvation of a sinner? _____

_____

_____

2. Compare the phrase "sins have been covered" (4:7) with faith "reckoned to him as righteousness." _____

_____

_____

3. In what sense was the rite of circumcision a *sign* or *seal* (4:11)? _____

4. What value did God place on faith in His promises to Abraham? _____

_____

_____

APPLICATIONS

1. The phrase "reckoned...as righteousness" may sound cold, but think of what is involved: the righteous God clothes the sinner with Christ's righteousness, and so there is one-to-one fellowship. Also, observe that David calls the man happy ("blessed") whose sins have been forgiven. List the things that bring you happiness, traced back to this, the forgiveness of your sins.

_____

_____

_____

_____

_____

_____

2. Works do not bring salvation. But works are an important fruit of the saved heart. Why is this? (Cf. James 2:14-26.)

_____

_____

_____

Summary of Passage

Whoever believes in God who justifies the ungodly, his faith is reckoned as righteousness. Neither works, religious rites, or the Law can save a sinner. Only faith can do that.

Memory Verses   4:7,8

Looking Ahead

Paul continues to write about Abraham's faith, but the focus is on the God whom Abraham believed.

SETTING In the preceding passage Paul had shown that God reckoned Abraham's faith as righteousness. Now he expands on this theme, emphasizing especially the omnipotent character of God.

Book of Romans: GOD'S SALVATION FOR SINNER

P R O L O G U E	NEED OF SALVATION	WAY OF SALVATION	LIFE OF SALVATION	SCOPE OF SALVATION	SERVICES OF SALVATION	E P I L O G U E
		DOCTRINAL			PRACTICAL	
	GOD'S POWER	GOD'S GRACE	GOD'S HOLINESS	GOD'S SOVEREIGNTY	GOD'S GLORY	
1:1	1:18	3:21	6:1	9:1	12:1	15:1

LIFE-GIVING GOD

16 For this reason IT IS BY FAITH
   that it might be IN ACCORDANCE WITH GRACE,
   in order that the PROMISE may be
                  certain to ALL the descendants,
   not only to those who are of the Law,
   but also to those
         who are of the **FAITH of ABRAHAM**,
   who is the FATHER of us ALL
17   (as it is written, "A father
     of many nations have I made you") [Gen. 17:5]
   in the sight of
      Him whom he BELIEVED,
      even GOD,
   who
         (1) gives **life** to the **dead** and
         (2) **calls into being** that which does not exist.

OF ALL WHO BELIEVE

18 In HOPE against HOPE he **BELIEVED**,
   in order that he might become
            a **father of many nations**,
   according to that which had been spoken,
   "**So shall your descendants be.**"   [Gen. 15:5]
19 And without becoming weak in **faith**
   he **contemplated**
      (1) his own **body**,
         now as good as **dead**
         since he was about a hundred years old, and
      (2) the **deadness** of Sarah's womb;
20   yet, with respect to the PROMISE of GOD,
   he **did not waver in unbelief**,
   BUT
      (1) grew **strong** in FAITH,
      (2) giving GLORY to GOD, and
      (3) being **fully assured** that what He had **promised**,
               He was able also to **perform**.
22 Therefore also
   it was reckoned to him as **RIGHTEOUSNESS**.

FULFILLER OF PROMISES

23 Now not for his sake only was it written,
   that "it **was reckoned** to him,"
24 but for our sake also,
         to whom it **will be reckoned**,
   as those who
   BELIEVE in HIM
            who RAISED JESUS
               OUR LORD
            from the dead,
25   HE who was
   (1) **delivered up** because of our **transgressions**,
      and was
   (2) raised because of our **justification**.

RAISED JESUS

OBSERVATIONS

Key Words and Phrases

4:16 "father of us all" _____
   17 _____
   17 _____
   19 _____
   20 _____

21 _____
24 _____
25 _____
others: _____

Segment Survey

Read the three paragraphs and observe the references to the life-giving power of God. Note especially the references at the end of the first and third paragraphs.

What does Paul write about Jesus in the segment? _____
_____

What parts of each paragraph support the outline shown on the textual re-creation chart?

Paragraph Analysis

4:16-17

1. How does Paul relate the words faith, grace, and promise in verse 16?

_____
_____
_____

2. How does he bring us *all*, as believers, into the picture? _____
_____

3. Then he relates us all to God. What descriptions of God does he choose to cite here?

_____
_____
_____

4:18-22

1. These verses recall God's test of Abraham's faith. What was the impossible situation (v.19), described as "against hope" (v. 18)?

_____
_____
_____

2. In what ways does Paul describe Abraham's faith? _____
_____
_____
_____
_____
_____
_____

3. What motivated Abraham to believe God (v. 18)? _____

_____

_____

4:23-25

1. How does Paul relate Jesus to God?

_____

_____

2. How does he relate Jesus to the Christian?

_____

_____

_____

Related Verses

Gen. 18:14 _____

_____

Rom. 15:8,9 _____

_____

Heb. 11:12 _____

_____

Rom. 10:9 _____

_____

1 Peter 1:21 _____

_____

1 Cor. 15:17 _____

_____

2 Cor. 5:15 _____

_____

INTERPRETATIONS

1. "It is by faith" (4:16). The word "it" refers to "the promise," so the opening words may read, "Therefore, the promise comes by faith." (Relate this back to 4:13).

2. Many attributes of God may have been cited in verse 17, such as His omniscience. Why do you think Paul chose to focus on His omnipotence, as conqueror of death, and as Creator?

_____

_____

_____

3. What phrases in the second paragraph identify Abraham's struggle against weakening under the test? _____

_____

_____

4. "Delivered up because of our transgressions" (4:25). Jesus was delivered over to death for our sins. The resurrection signaled God's acceptance of Christ's substitutionary death, without which

we could not be justified. Compare 1 Peter 2:24 and Isaiah 53:5,6,8b,11.

APPLICATIONS

1. The Christian's God is the God of *life*. What occurs to you when you think about this? For example, does it give you peace of heart and joy to know that you have eternal life? And what about this present life? Jot down some things about your life that should serve as a testimony regarding the God of life.

_____

_____

_____

_____

_____

_____

_____

2. What do you learn from Abraham about faith in God for miracles? Abraham knew God would *perform*, because He had **promised**. How should you apply this in your prayer life? (TBS#4)

_____

_____

Summary of Passage

The believer's God is a life-giving God. He created all things; He gives life to the dead; He performs miracles. The grand miracle was His raising Jesus from the dead. It was because of our sins that Jesus was delivered over to death; and it was for our justification that God raised Him to life.

Memory Verses 4:20-21

Looking Ahead

Paul will bring all of this discussion to personal application by describing the fruits and blessings of justification.

SETTING In the preceding section Paul had shown reasons why the believer glories in the life-giving God. Now he focuses more on Jesus' death for us, and identifies the many fruits and blessings which the believer has.

Book of Romans: GOD'S SALVATION FOR SINNER

P R O L O G U E	NEED OF SALVATION	WAY OF SALVATION	LIFE OF SALVATION	SCOPE OF SALVATION	SERVICES OF SALVATION	E P I L O G U E
		DOCTRINAL			PRACTICAL	
	GOD'S POWER	GOD'S GRACE	GOD'S HOLINESS	GOD'S SOVEREIGNTY	GOD'S GLORY	
1:1	1:18	3:21	6:1	9:1	12:1	15:1

others: _____

_____

Segment Survey

What is the prominent *pronoun* of this passage? Paul joins with all Christians in rejoicing over salvation in Christ Jesus. Cf. the phrases "to all" (4:16) and "for our sake also" (4:24).

What is the *tone* of the segment?

_____

_____

Observe the appearances of the word "exult."

The segment may be divided into three paragraphs, around *time*. Observe this sequence as you read the text: present, past, future. Note the outline shown on the chart.

Compare the first and last verses of the segment.

_____

_____

_____

_____

Paragraph Analysis

5:1-5

1. Examine carefully the first two verses, which form one sentence. Show the main construction of thought by filling in this diagram:

    WE HAVE _____

       through _____

     and through _____

    WE EXULT _____

2. In what else does Paul rejoice (v. 3)?

_____

How does he relate this to hope, in verses 3-5?

_____

_____

Note that hope is mentioned last in the list as the highest factor.

3. What ministry of the Holy Spirit does he write about in verse 5?

5:6-8

1. What are the two references to "while we were"? _____

_____

2. What does this reveal about God's love to man?

_____

_____

WHY CHRISTIANS REJOICE

WHAT WE HAVE

1 Therefore having been JUSTIFIED BY FAITH,
    we have PEACE with GOD
          through OUR LORD JESUS CHRIST,
2   through whom also
    we have obtained our
      introduction BY FAITH
      into this grace in which we stand;
    and we exult in HOPE of the GLORY of GOD.
3 And not only this, but
      we exult in our TRIBULATIONS;
    knowing that
      tribulation brings about perseverance; and
4   perseverance, ⟶ proven character; and
    proven character, ⟶ hope; and
5   hope does not disappoint;
    because
      the LOVE OF GOD has been poured out
         (1) within our hearts
         (2) through the Holy Spirit
            who was given to us.

WHAT WE WERE

6 For while we were still HELPLESS,
     at the right time
        CHRIST DIED FOR THE UNGODLY.
7 For one will hardly die for a righteous man;
    though perhaps for the good man
       someone would dare even to die.
8 But God demonstrates
      HIS OWN LOVE TOWARD US,
    in that while we were yet SINNERS,
      CHRIST DIED FOR US.

WHAT SHALL BE

9 Much more then,
    having now been JUSTIFIED
        by HIS BLOOD,
    we shall be SAVED
      from the wrath of God
        through HIM.
10 For if while we were enemies,
    we were RECONCILED TO GOD
         through the DEATH of HIS SON,
    much more, having been RECONCILED,
         we shall be SAVED by His LIFE.
11 And not only this,
    but we also exult in God
        through our Lord Jesus Christ,
    through whom we have NOW RECEIVED
      THE RECONCILIATION.

OBSERVATIONS

Key Words and Phrases

5:1 "peace with God"
2 _____
3 _____
5 _____
6 _____
9 _____
10 _____
11 _____

5:9-11

1. Compare "justified by His blood" (v. 9) with "justified by faith" (v. 1)._____

2. Also compare the remainder of each of the verses._____

3. Observe the future tense of the repeated phrase "we shall be saved" (vv. 9,10). In each case, what are we saved from?

_____

Related Verses

Heb. 7:25_____

Eph. 2:18_____

Rom. 8:23_____

1 Thess. 1:10_____

2 Thess. 1:9_____

Phil. 3:20-21_____

1 Peter 1:3-7_____

INTERPRETATIONS

1. What does it mean to have "peace with God" (5:1)? What alienates man from God? What do the phrases "wrath of God" (5:9) and "reconciliation" (5:11) suggest about man's problem?

_____

2. The word "introduction" (5:2) means "access." Relate this to "peace with God."

_____

3. What does the short word "for" mean in the statement "Christ died for us" (5:8)?

_____

4. Why would Christ have to *die* to save us from God's wrath (5:9)? _____

5. There are three aspects of salvation: (1) *positional*—we are declared righteous; (2) *progressive*—we are being conformed more and more into the image of Christ (Rom. 8:29); (3) *final*—we shall be like Jesus forever (1 John 3:2), and body, soul and spirit will be perfect. The phrase "shall be saved" (verses 9 and 10) refers mainly to final salvation.

APPLICATIONS

1. What do you learn from this passage about:
a. the ministry of the Holy Spirit in your heart (TBS#3)_____

b. how you can rejoice in tribulations

_____

2. How much do you value your privilege of access to God through Jesus? How much are you using this, and growing in your spiritual stature? Suggest how you can improve this relationship.

_____

Summary of Passage

As Christians, we can rejoice because we have peace with God through our Lord Jesus Christ, and also because God pours His love into our hearts. Our Christian hope assures us of eternal salvation and gives us the joy of offering even our tribulations to God, for His glory.

A Memory Verse   5:8

Looking Ahead

The spotlight is on the *free gift* of God by contrasting it with death brought about by sin.

SETTING This closing segment of the doctrinal section is called WAY OF SALVATION. Note on the survey chart that God's grace is prominent in the section.

Book of Romans: GOD'S SALVATION FOR SINNER

P R O L O G U E	NEED OF SALVATION	WAY OF SALVATION	LIFE OF SALVATION	SCOPE OF SALVATION	SERVICES OF SALVATION	E P I L O G U E
		DOCTRINAL			PRACTICAL	
	GOD'S POWER	GOD'S GRACE	GOD'S HOLINESS	GOD'S SOVEREIGNTY	GOD'S GLORY	
1:1	1:18	3:21	6:1	9:1	12:1	15:

THE FREE GIFT

12 Therefore, just as through one man
    SIN entered into the world,
    and **death** through sin,
    and so death spread to ALL MEN,
                because ALL SINNED—

13 for until the LAW sin was in the world;
    but sin is NOT IMPUTED when there is no law.
14 Nevertheless
        death reigned from ADAM until MOSES,
    even over those
  who had not sinned in the likeness of the offense
    of Adam,
      who is a type of **Him who was to come.**

15 But the FREE GIFT
           is not like the TRANSGRESSION.
  For if by **the transgression** of the one
          the many DIED,
  much more did the GRACE of GOD
      and the GIFT
      by the GRACE of the one Man,
           JESUS CHRIST,
        abound to the many.

16 And the GIFT is **not** like
    that which came through
      the one who sinned;
  for on the one hand
      the JUDGMENT arose
        from one TRANSGRESSION
          resulting in CONDEMNATION,
  but on the other hand
      the FREE GIFT **arose**
        from many TRANSGRESSIONS
          resulting in JUSTIFICATION.
17 For if by **the transgression** of the one,
    DEATH REIGNED through the one,
  much more → those who receive the **abundance**
    (1) **of GRACE** and
    (2) of the **GIFT** of RIGHTEOUSNESS
  will REIGN IN LIFE
      through the One, JESUS CHRIST.

18 So then **as** through one TRANSGRESSION
    there resulted CONDEMNATION to all men,
    even so through one ACT of RIGHTEOUSNESS
    there resulted JUSTIFICATION of LIFE to all men.
19 For **as** through the one man's DISOBEDIENCE
    the many were made **sinners,**
  even so through the OBEDIENCE of the One
    the many will be made **righteous.**
20   And the LAW came in
    that the **transgression** might **increase;**
  but **where** sin increased,
      GRACE ABOUNDED all the more,
21 that, **as** sin reigned in death,
  even so GRACE MIGHT REIGN
      through RIGHTEOUSNESS
      to ETERNAL LIFE
      through
          Jesus Christ
          our Lord.

(vertical labels: LIKENESSES, CONTRASTS, LIKENESSES)

OBSERVATIONS

Key Words and Phrases

5:12 "sin"

12 _____

15 _____

15 _____

15 _____

15 _____

15 _____

20 _____

others: _____

Segment Survey

There is a long parenthesis (vv. 13-17) in the middle of this segment. The "as" clause of verse 12 does not find its sequel until verse 18. Try reading verse 12 immediately followed by verses 18-21, noting the continuity of thought. Then go back and read the parenthesis of verses 13-17. Mark this parenthesis on the textual re-creation chart.

The two main paragraphs (first and last) are about the likenesses of Adam and Jesus ("as...even so").

The two parenthetical paragraphs bring out the *contrasts* of the two ("the free gift is not like").

Paragraph Analysis

5:12 and 5:18-21
1. List the similarities of these paragraphs. One example is shown.

    one man (Adam)—12,19   one man (Christ)—1?

_____

_____

_____

_____

_____

_____

_____

2. What are the climactic phrases of verse 21?

_____

_____

_____

_____

_____

How do these phrases help you sense what Paul was feeling as he wrote these lines?

_____

_____

5:13-14

Was there a penalty for sins of those living between Adam and Moses, even though the sins did not break commands, as Adam's sin did? If so, what was that penalty?

_____

_____

5:15-17

1. Mark on the textual re-creation every place where the words "gift" and "grace" appear.
2. List the contrasts you find in the paragraph.

transgression of Adam—15   grace of Jesus—15

_____

_____

_____

_____

_____

3. Compare verse 17 with verses 20-21.

_____

_____

Related Verses

Isa. 53:11 _____

_____

Phil. 2:8 _____

_____

Gal. 3:19 _____

_____

John 3:16 _____

_____

John 1:1-5 _____

_____

2 Cor. 5:17 _____

_____

INTERPRETATIONS

1. "Because all sinned" (5:12). When Adam sinned, every member of the human race, yet unborn, sinned. Adam was both the individual *and* the race. This is the solidarity or unity of the human race. "As the whole lies in the germ, the oak in the acorn, so all humanity resides in Adam and, by grace through faith, also in Christ. As we are a physical, so also are we a spiritual organism." (F. Davidson and Ralph P. Martin, *New Bible Commentary*, p. 1026)

2. "Death reigned" (5:14). The strongest proof that sin was sin even before God gave the written Law is that "death reigned from Adam until Moses" (5:14). The judgment of death for Adam's sin is recorded in Genesis 3:14 ff.

3. As Adam was the federal head of the human race, Christ is the federal Head of a *new* race composed of believers, all of whom partake of His divine nature. Any child of Adam may, by simple faith, be identified with the new race of Christ. Read the passage again and note references to those who appropriate the free gift of Christ's righteousness. Record these here.

_____

_____

_____

APPLICATIONS

1. What are your thoughts about God's grace to you, now that you have spent much time in this portion of His Word?

_____

_____

What do you want to share with an unbeliever about this, as you witness to him? For example, what phrases of the Bible text would you especially bring to his attention?

_____

_____

_____

_____

_____

_____

_____

Summary of Passage

As sin entered the world through one man, even so sinners may be made righteous through the death of one man, Christ, by believing in Him. Just as sin reigns in death, grace reigns through righteousness to eternal life through Jesus Christ the Lord.

Memory Verses   5:20b-21

Looking Ahead

Paul will begin to write about how to live the Christian life. It is the natural follow-up of the section you have just studied—about how to become a Christian.

LIFE OF
SALVATION
6:1–8:39

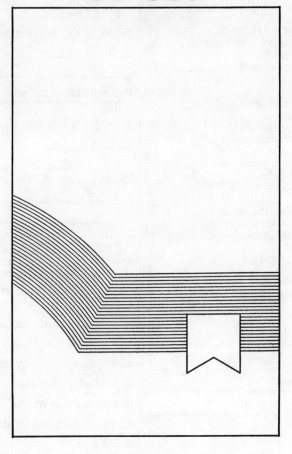

SETTING Note on the survey chart that at this point in his letter Paul begins to write about the LIFE OF SALVATION. The saved person needs to know *how to live the Christian life.* Among other things, Paul will show in chapters 6–8 that God's power helps him in this day-by-day living.

Book of Romans: GOD'S SALVATION FOR SINNER

P R O L O G U E	NEED OF SALVATION	WAY OF SALVATION	LIFE OF SALVATION	SCOPE OF SALVATION	SERVICES OF SALVATION	
		DOCTRINAL			PRACTICAL	
	GOD'S POWER	GOD'S GRACE	GOD'S HOLINESS	GOD'S SOVEREIGNTY	GOD'S GLORY	
1:1	1:18	3:21	6:1	9:1	12:1	15:

Segment Survey

Note that Paul opens the segment with questions. Relate these to the things he had just written, especially 5:20-21.

_____

_____

Read the segment, looking for action words about Christian *living.* Mark these on the chart.

Observe that Paul is teaching our identity with Christ. Look for words such as "with," "in" and "into."

The segment has two paragraphs, and your analysis of them will show how the first leads into the second.

What is the key command of the segment?

_____

_____

DEAD BUT ALIVE

1 What shall we say THEN?
    Are we to **continue in** sin
      that grace might increase?
2   May it never be!
    How shall we who **died to sin** still **live in it?**
3 Or do you not know
    that all of us
      who have been **baptized into Christ Jesus**
      have been baptized into HIS DEATH?
4 Therefore we have been **buried with Him**
      through **baptism into death,**
in order that
  as CHRIST WAS RAISED
    from the dead
    through the GLORY of the FATHER,
so we too might WALK IN NEWNESS OF LIFE.

DEATH IDENTITY

5 For if we have become **united with Him**
    in the **likeness of His death,**
  certainly we shall be also
    in the **likeness of His resurrection,**
6   knowing this,
  that **our old self** was crucified with Him,
  (1) that our BODY OF SIN might be done away with,
  (2) that we should no longer be SLAVES TO SIN;
7   for ——→ he who has **died** is **freed from sin.**
8 Now if we have **died with Christ,**
  we believe that we shall also live with Him,
9 knowing that CHRIST,
    having been **raised from the dead,**
      IS NEVER TO DIE AGAIN;
    death no longer is MASTER over Him. ◄——
10 For the death that He died,
  He died **to sin,** ONCE for ALL;
  but the life that He lives,
    He lives to God.
11 Even so ——→ CONSIDER yourselves to be
           DEAD TO SIN,
        but ALIVE TO GOD
        in Christ Jesus.

DEATH-AND-LIFE IDENTITY

OBSERVATIONS

Key Words and Phrases

6:1   "continue in sins" _____

  2_____

  3_____

  4_____

  5_____

  6_____

  9_____

  11_____

others:_____

_____

Paragraph Analysis

6:1-4

1. What is the last phrase of the paragraph?

_____

_____

What phrase of the first verse is in contrast to this? _____

_____

2. This is the first appearance of the words "baptized" and "baptism" in the letter. The spiritual intent of the word is that of *identification.* (See **INTERPRETATIONS**.) Complete the following sequence, based on phrases of the Bible text:

a. we have been baptized into Christ

b. we have been baptized into His _____

c. we _____ to sin

d. Christ was raised from the dead

e. our walk is one of _____

4. we should not be living in _____

6:5-11

1. Observe the words "certainly" and "knowing" in the paragraph. How do the words relate to the concluding command, "consider" (v. 11)?

_____

_____

_____

_____

_____

_____

2. Record the references to resurrection and life:

_____

_____

3. How does Paul relate sins and sinning to death with Christ?_____

How does he relate victory over sins to life with Christ? _____

Related Verses

Gal. 2:20_____

_____

Gal. 3:26-27_____

_____

Col. 2:12 _____

_____

1 Peter 3:18_____

_____

Heb. 9:12 _____

_____

Heb. 9:26-28_____

_____

Heb. 10:10_____

_____

INTERPRETATIONS

1. When a sinner is saved, he is joined to Christ. This baptism into Christ's death separates him from the old life ("our old self was crucified with Him," v. 6), and associates him with the new life ("alive to God in Christ Jesus," v. 11). Paul writes that this identification with Christ's resurrection makes it possible for the Christian to "walk in newness of life" (6:4).

2. Death is essentially a separation (e.g. physical death is separation of the body from the spirit). Paul is teaching in this passage that death to sin is separation from the mastery, or ruling power, of sin. Compare verses 6 and 9.

_____

_____

_____

_____

_____

_____

APPLICATIONS

1. In your own words, based on your study of this passage, answer Paul's question of verse 2.

_____

_____

_____

_____

_____

_____

_____

2. Paul's testimony about the death/life identity is recorded in Galatians, the first epistle he wrote. Read Galatians 2:20. Then apply the verse to some situation that may be part of your experience today, such as resisting a temptation or making a decision. Record how you expect to have victory in the situation.

_____

_____

_____

_____

_____

_____

_____

_____

Summary of Passage

As Christians, our old self was crucified with Christ, so we are to consider ourselves dead to sin. Also, as Christ was raised from the dead, so we are to consider ourselves alive to God, walking in newness of life.

A Memory Verse   6:11

Looking Ahead

Paul will appeal to believers to present their whole beings to God as slaves to righteousness.

SETTING The preceding passage (6:1-11) was about the death/life identity which believers *know* to be true. This passage is the command to put that principle to work in daily living.

Book of Romans: GOD'S SALVATION FOR SINNER

P R O L O G U E	NEED OF SALVATION	WAY OF SALVATION	LIFE OF SALVATION	SCOPE OF SALVATION	SERVICES OF SALVATION	E P I L O G U E
		DOCTRINAL			PRACTICAL	
	GOD'S POWER	GOD'S GRACE	GOD'S HOLINESS	GOD'S SOVEREIGNTY	GOD'S GLORY	
1:1	1:18	3:21	6:1	9:1	12:1	15:1

PRESENT YOURSELVES TO GOD

12 Therefore **do not let** sin REIGN in your mortal BODY
      that you should OBEY ITS LUSTS,
13   and **do not go on presenting**
     the members of your BODY to SIN
      as instruments of UNRIGHTEOUSNESS;
     but PRESENT YOURSELVES TO GOD
        as those **alive** from the dead,
      and YOUR MEMBERS
      as instruments of RIGHTEOUSNESS to God
14 For SIN shall NOT BE **MASTER OVER YOU,**
    for you are not under law,
      but under GRACE. ◄

APPEAL

15 What then?
    Shall we sin because we are not under law
        but under GRACE?
      May it never be!
16 Do you not know that
    when you PRESENT yourselves to someone
      as SLAVES for OBEDIENCE,
    you are **slaves** of the one whom you **obey,**
    either
      (1) of SIN resulting in DEATH,
    or
      (2) of Obedience resulting in RIGHTEOUSNESS?
17 But THANKS BE TO GOD
    that though you **WERE** slaves of sin,
    you **BECAME** obedient from the heart
      to that form of teaching
      to which you were committed,
18 and having been **freed from sin,**
     you BECAME slaves of RIGHTEOUSNESS

YOU WERE

19 I am speaking in **human** terms
        because of the weakness of your flesh.
  For just as you **presented** your members
    as slaves to impurity
    and to lawlessness,
      resulting in further lawlessness,
  so now
    PRESENT YOUR MEMBERS
    AS SLAVES to **righteousness,**
        resulting in SANCTIFICATION.
20 For when you **were slaves of sin,**
      you were free in regard to righteousness.
21 Therefore what benefit were you then deriving
    from the things of which you are now ashamed?
    For the OUTCOME of those things is DEATH.
22 But now having been
        (1) freed from sin
  and
        (2) enslaved to God,
  you derive your benefit,
  resulting in
        (1) SANCTIFICATION
  and
        (2) the outcome, ETERNAL LIFE.
23 For THE WAGES OF SIN is DEATH,
    BUT THE FREE GIFT OF GOD
          is ETERNAL LIFE
    in Christ Jesus our Lord.

BUT NOW

OBSERVATIONS
Key Words and Phrases

6:13 "presenting the members"

13 _____

14 _____

16 _____

18 _____

19 _____

22 _____

23 _____

others: _____

Segment Survey

The segment contains three paragraphs, the first of which is a connector because it concludes the preceding paragraph and introduces the paragraphs that follow it.

Although there are many key repeated words, the most prominent one is "present." Read the segment and mark its appearances in the textual re-creation.

The opening paragraph introduces the subject of presenting oneself to someone. Then in the second paragraph Paul refers to what his readers did before they were saved. This leads him to the present appeal, following the words "so now" (6:19).

Paragraph Analysis
6:12-14
The paragraph is made up of doctrinal *facts* and practical *commands*. List them:

FACTS: _____

_____

_____

COMMANDS: _____

_____

_____

_____

6:15-18
1. Compare 6:15 with 6:1. Then compare it with

6:14. _____

_____

2. The *Living Bible* paraphrases verse 15: "Does this mean that we can now go ahead and sin and not worry about it? ... Of course not!" Record how

Paul then argues against license to sin:

principle of verse 16: _____

_____

believer's past experiences: _____

_____

3. Note the repeated word "obedience." How is it a key to Paul's argument?

_____

_____

6:19-23

1. Note the past and the present in verse 19. What is the command of the verse?

_____

What one word identifies the fruit of the command? _____

2. Note the past and the present in verses 20-22. What are the fruits of the new servitude, 6:22?

_____

3. How does 6:23 relate to the preceding verses of the paragraph? _____

_____

Related Verses

1 Cor. 9:21 _____

_____

Col. 2:6-7 _____

_____

Rom. 8:2,12,13 _____

_____

Phil. 3:21 _____

_____

1 Cor. 1:2,30 _____

_____

1 John 3:2 _____

INTERPRETATIONS

1. "Freed from sin" (6:18) does not mean sinless perfection. Earlier (verse 14), Paul had written that "sin shall not be master over you." So now, when he says that the believer has been freed from sin, he means free from the mastery or controlling power of sin.

2. At the new birth, a Christian, who had been a slave of sin (v. 17), now becomes a slave of righteousness (v. 18) and of God (v. 22). As a new creature in Christ, he must present his members (whole being) as instruments of righteousness to God (v. 13).

3. There are three aspects of sanctification (lit. *holiness*) in the Christian's life: (See Unit 13.)

a. past *(positional)*. The sinner becomes a saint (same root as "sanctification") the moment he is saved. This is his position in Christ. (Cf. Rom. 6:16b.)

b. present *(experiential)*. This is a growth in spiritual maturity, depending on yieldedness (the appeal of Rom. 6:19b).

c. future *(final)*. This sinless state begins "at home with the Lord." (Cf. Rom. 6:22,23; 2 Cor. 5:8.)

APPLICATIONS

1. Who is the believer's master? What comes to your mind when you think of a master?

_____

_____

How important is *obedience* in the Christian walk? Write down some commands from your Master that you can recall, which apply to every waking hour of your life. _____

_____

_____

_____

2. What help do you have in getting victory over sin each day? Discuss this with your group. (TBS#'s 1-7) _____

_____

_____

_____

_____

_____

_____

Summary of Passage

As a child of God, I must present my whole being to Him in righteousness and obedience, and this devotion brings forth sanctification, and the outcome, eternal life.

Memory Verses   6:22-23

Looking Ahead

Paul will illustrate the Christian's walk in another way—living in freedom from the Law.

SETTING This passage on liberation forms the last segment on PRINCIPLES OF CHRISTIAN LIVING:

(1) double identification (dead and alive)
      6:1-11
(2) new servitude (before and after)
      6:12-23
(3) total liberation (old and new)
      7:1-6

RELEASED FROM THE LAW

1 Or do you not know, brethren
      (for I am speaking to those who know the law),
      that the law has **jurisdiction** over a person
            as long as he **lives**?
2 For the **married woman** is bound by law
      to **her husband** while he is **living**;
      but if her husband **dies**,
            she is released from the law
                        concerning her husband.
3 So then if, while her husband is **living**,
            she is joined to another man,
            she shall be called AN ADULTERESS;
      but if her husband **dies**,
            she is free from the law
      so that she is **not** AN ADULTERESS,
            though she is joined to another man.

PRINCIPLE

4 Therefore, my brethren,
      you also were made to **die to the Law**
                        through the BODY OF CHRIST,
      that you might be
            joined to another,
            to Him who was RAISED FROM THE DEAD,
                  that we might bear FRUIT FOR GOD.
5 For while we were in the flesh,
            the SINFUL PASSIONS,
                        which were **aroused by the Law**,
            were at work
            in the members of our BODY
                        to bear FRUIT FOR DEATH.
6 BUT NOW
      we have been RELEASED from the LAW,
            having DIED
                  to that by which we were BOUND,
      so that WE SERVE
                  in NEWNESS of the Spirit
      and **not**
                  in OLDNESS of the LETTER.

APPLICATION

OBSERVATIONS

Key Words and Phrases

7:1 ___ "the law" ___

   2 _____

   3 _____

   4 _____

   4 _____

   5 _____

   6 _____

others: _____

_____

Book of Romans: GOD'S SALVATION FOR SINNER

P R O L O G U E	NEED OF SALVATION	WAY OF SALVATION	LIFE OF SALVATION	SCOPE OF SALVATION	SERVICES OF SALVATION	E P I L O G U E
			DOCTRINAL		PRACTICAL	
	GOD'S POWER	GOD'S GRACE	GOD'S HOLINESS	GOD'S SOVEREIGNTY	GOD'S GLORY	
1:1	1:18	3:21	6:1	9:1	12:1	15:1

Segment Survey

The segment has two paragraphs. Read these. Note the opening phrase of the second paragraph. What is the prominent pronoun of the first paragraph? _____

Why does the repeated pronoun of the first lines of the second paragraph change from "you" to "we"? _____

_____

Justify the two-point outline: PRINCIPLE; APPLICATION.

What key repeated words stand out in this segment? _____

_____

_____

Note the phrase, "the law," in the first paragraph, and "the Law" in the second. How does this support the above outline?

_____

_____

_____

Paragraph Analysis

7:1-3
1. What principle does Paul state in verse 1?

_____

_____

2. How is this illustrated by legislation concerning marriage (7:2)? _____

_____

3. What are the two examples described in verse 3? _____

_____

_____

4. Note the word "bound" in verse 2. What two contrasting words appear in the remainder of the paragraph? _____

_____

7:4-6
1. The "body of Christ" (v. 4) means the death of Christ. In the illustration of verse 4, who or what dies with Christ: the believer, or the Jewish Law?

_____

_____

Then what union takes place?

What is the fruit of this new union?

2. What activity and living does verse 5 describe, *before* the death-to-the-Law experience of verse 4? What was the fruit of that old union?

3. What experience brings about release from the Law (v. 6)?

How is the new life described in verse 6a?

Related Verses

Rom. 6:4,13

Rom. 6:20,21

Rom. 8:2

Gal. 2:19

2 Cor. 3:6; Jer. 31:31 ff.

Col. 1:22

INTERPRETATIONS

1. "You were made to die to the Law" (7:4). This is release from bondage to the Law, which is also bondage to sin. (Cf. 7:7.) At 6:6 Paul had described it this way: "our old self was crucified with Him, ... that we should no longer be slaves to sin."

2. "In the flesh" (7:5). This is the life of man in his sinful human nature, without the help of the Spirit of God. It is a life of sinful indulgence. NIV translates, "For when we were controlled by our sinful nature."

3. What do you think is meant by the phrase, "fruit for death" (7:5)?

4. What meaning is suggested by the words, "newness of the Spirit" (7:6)?

APPLICATIONS

1. Before you were saved, sinful passions were at work in your body, identified by the Commandments of God ("Thou shalt" and "Thou shalt not"). What kind of fruit did that life bring forth?

2. Now that you have been crucified with Christ (Gal. 2:20), you are released from the bondage of the Law and are joined to the risen Christ to bear fruit for God. What kind of fruit is this, in the course of a day of your life? Bring 6:22 into your answer.

Are some fruits lacking, or marred, in your life? If so, why not seek the Lord's help to do something about this?

Summary of Passage

A man without Christ is in bondage to the Law, and the sinful passions aroused by that Law bear fruit for death. When he is saved, he is crucified with Christ, and this death frees him from the Law's bondage. This brings him into union with the risen Christ, and the freed life bears fruit for God.

A Memory Verse   7:6

Looking Ahead

At 7:7 Paul begins to focus more on the *practice* of everyday living, having written much on the *principle* involved (6:1–7:6).

SETTING Paul has just written that the Christian has been released from the Law (7:6). Such a statement makes the Law *appear* to be evil. So in this segment he shows that the Law is good.

Book of Romans: GOD'S SALVATION FOR SINNER

P R O L O G U E	NEED OF SALVATION	WAY OF SALVATION	LIFE OF SALVATION	SCOPE OF SALVATION	SERVICES OF SALVATION	E P I L O G U E
			DOCTRINAL		PRACTICAL	
	GOD'S POWER	GOD'S GRACE	GOD'S HOLINESS	GOD'S SOVEREIGNTY	GOD'S GLORY	
1:1	1:18	3:21	6:1	9:1	12:1	15:1

THE LAW AND SIN

7 What shall we say then?
    Is the Law sin?
                May it never be!
On the contrary,
    I would not have come to **know sin**
            except through the LAW;
for I would not have known about COVETING
        if the LAW had not said,
    "You shall not covet."   [Ex. 20:17]   *LAW*

8 But SIN,
    taking opportunity through the commandment,
    PRODUCED IN ME
    coveting of every kind;   [Deut. 5:21]
    for **apart** from the Law
       sin is dead.
9 And I was once ALIVE apart from the LAW;
    but when the commandment came,
       sin became alive
        and I died;
10 and this commandment,
    which was to result in LIFE,
       proved to result in DEATH for me;
11 for SIN,
    taking opportunity through the commandment,
    DECEIVED ME,
       and through it killed me.
12 So then,
    (1) the Law is HOLY, and
    (2) the commandment is HOLY
          and RIGHTEOUS and GOOD.   *SIN*

13 Therefore did that which is GOOD
    become a cause of **DEATH FOR ME?**
           May it never be!
Rather it was SIN,
    in order that it might be shown to be SIN
       by effecting **MY DEATH**   *SUMMARY*
         through that which is GOOD,
    that through the COMMANDMENT
           SIN might become UTTERLY SINFUL.

OBSERVATIONS

Key Words and Phrases

7:7 ____ "the Law" _____
  7 _____
  8 _____
  9 _____
 10 _____
 11 _____
 12 _____
 13 _____
others: _____
_____

Segment Survey

This brief segment may be divided into three paragraphs: LAW, SIN, SUMMARY. Read the segment and justify this outline.

What are the two most prominent repeated words? _____
_____

What is the opening question?
_____
_____

Where is it answered?
_____

What other question does Paul ask?
_____
_____

Paragraph Analysis

7:7
1. What was the statement about the Law (7:6) which brought on the question of this paragraph?
_____
_____

2. In your own words, what is Paul's answer?
_____
_____
_____

7:8-12
1. Analyze the paragraph around the three statements of verse 9 shown below. Record what is revealed in the paragraph about each.

THE LAW CAME: _____
_____
_____
_____

SIN BECAME ALIVE: _____
_____
_____
_____

I DIED: _____
_____
_____
_____

2. How is verse 12 an answer to the question of verse 7? _____
_____
_____

7:13

1. Observe that Paul concludes that the Law does not *cause* death. How does he carefully word this in verse 10?_____

_____

2. Throughout the passage, what is it that brings death?_____

_____

3. What statement of verse 13 shows how *utterly* sinful sin is?_____

_____

_____

Related Verses

Gen. 3:11,13,17_____

_____

Deut. 5:21_____

_____

Rom. 3:20_____

_____

Rom. 5:20,21_____

_____

1 Cor. 15:56_____

_____

1 Tim. 1:8 ff._____

_____

Rev. 12:9_____

_____

INTERPRETATIONS

1. "I would not have known about coveting" (7:7). Before the Law was given, everyone had thoughts and desires of having what was not theirs. With the arrival of the Law, they learned that this was sin (Ex. 20:17). So it was from the Law that they got to *know* about coveting.

2. "Sin ... deceived me" (7:11). Paul personalizes sin. The deceiver is Satan. See Revelation 12:9.

3. "Killed me" (7:11). This is because "the wages of sin is death" (6:23).

4. Note the three adjectives describing the Law in verse 12. What is meant by each?

HOLY_____

_____

RIGHTEOUS_____

_____

GOOD_____

_____

5. Sin is "utterly sinful" (7:13). What does this mean, according to the context?

_____

APPLICATIONS

1. Deceit is one of Satan's main weapons in tempting people to sin. Write a list of various sins, and identify how Satan deceives in connection with each.

_____

_____

_____

_____

_____

2. The Law is good. What about the commands of Scripture, directed to you as a believer? How do you appreciate them? Which kinds do you have the most difficulty obeying? Do you know why? What can you do to help in this weakness?

_____

_____

_____

_____

_____

_____

_____

Summary of Passage

The Law is holy, righteous and good. It reveals what sin is. It does not cause death, but death comes to those who sin by breaking it.

A Memory Verse   7:7

Looking Ahead

Paul deals head-on with the problem of sins in the believer's life.

SETTING Paul has just written about the Law and sin. Now he writes about the conflict in the human heart over sinning, because of the presence of the law of sin and Law of God.

Book of Romans: GOD'S SALVATION FOR SINNER

P R O L O G U E	NEED OF SALVATION	WAY OF SALVATION	LIFE OF SALVATION	SCOPE OF SALVATION	SERVICES OF SALVATION	E P I L O G U E
			DOCTRINAL		PRACTICAL	
	GOD'S POWER	GOD'S GRACE	GOD'S HOLINESS	GOD'S SOVEREIGNTY	GOD'S GLORY	
1:1	1:18	3:21	6:1	9:1	12:1	15:1

CONFLICTING LAWS

14 For we know that THE LAW IS **SPIRITUAL**;
    but I am
        (1) of flesh,
        (2) sold into **bondage to sin**.
15 For that which I am **doing**,
                            I do not **understand**;
    for I am not practicing
            what I would like to do,
            but I am doing the **very thing** I HATE.
16 But if
        I do the **very thing**
        I do not wish to do,
        I agree with the Law,
    confessing that IT IS GOOD.
17 **So now**, no longer am I the one doing it,
            but SIN which indwells me.
18 For I know
    that NOTHING GOOD DWELLS IN ME,
                        that is, IN MY FLESH;
        for the **wishing** is present in me,
        but the **doing** of the good is **not**.
19 For the **GOOD** that I **wish**,
                    I do not do;
        but I practice the very evil
                    that I do not **wish**.
20 But if I am **doing**
        the very thing I do not **wish**,
    I am no longer the one doing it,
        but SIN which dwells in me.

CONFLICTING DESIRES

21   I find **then** the PRINCIPLE that
    EVIL IS PRESENT in
        me,
        the one who **wishes to do good**.
22 For I joyfully concur with the Law of God
                    in the inner **man**,
23 but I see a **different** law
        in the members of my BODY,
    waging WAR against the law of my MIND,
    and making me a PRISONER of the law of sin
            which is in my members.

CONFLICTING LAWS

24 WRETCHED MAN THAT I AM!
    Who will **set me free**
                from the BODY OF THIS DEATH?
25   THANKS BE TO GOD
    through Jesus Christ our Lord!
    So then,
        on the one hand I myself with my MIND
            am SERVING THE Law of God,
        but **on the other**, with my FLESH
                    THE law of sin.

ONE ANSWER

OBSERVATIONS

Key Words and Phrases

7:14 "the Law" _____

15 _____

16 _____

18 _____

19 _____

23 _____
24 _____
24 _____
others: _____
_____

Segment Survey

Read the segment and observe the many key repeated words and phrases.

Note that the segment is divided into three paragraphs. Do you detect conflicting desires and wishes in the first long paragraph?

What does the second paragraph add to the first?

_____
_____

How is the last paragraph a fitting conclusion to the segment? _____
_____
_____

Paragraph Analysis

7:14-20

1. How does the opening line refer to the preceding segment?

_____
_____

How does Paul identify himself in verse 14?

_____
_____

What more does he say about this in verse 18?

_____
_____
_____

What part of him does he mean by "in my flesh"?

_____
_____

2. What was Paul's inner conflict?

_____
_____
_____

3. Is he excusing or indicting himself in verse 20? Explain. _____
_____
_____
_____
_____

7:21-23

1. What references to law do you see here?

_____

_____

2. Between what two laws is there a war (7:23)?

_____

_____

3. Of what does the first law make Paul prisoner?

_____

_____

7:24-25

1. What brought on Paul's exclamation of verse 24a? _____

_____

2. What does he cry out for? What is significant about the word "Who" at this place in his discussion? _____

_____

3. What is the answer?

_____

_____

4. How does the segment conclude (7:25b)?

_____

_____

Related Verses

Rom. 8:2 _____

_____

1 Cor. 15:56,57 _____

_____

Gal. 5:16-18 _____

_____

Eph. 3:16 _____

_____

1 Peter 2:11 _____

_____

James 4:1 _____

INTERPRETATIONS

1. "Sin which indwells me" (7:17). Combining verses 16 and 17, Paul is saying that sin which indwells him does the very thing he does not wish to do. What does he mean here by "sin," based on what he has taught earlier in the epistle? Compare this also with what he says about his flesh, in verse 18a.

_____

_____

_____

_____

2. "A different law in the members of my body" (7:23). This was the law of Paul's body (the doer of the evil deeds) which warred against the law of his mind (the wisher of good).

3. "The body of this death" (7:24). Paul is not asking to be freed from the body as such (which would be physical death), but from the body characterized by the spiritual death about which he has been writing. This goes back to verse 23, where Paul shows the body to be the scene of the battle.

4. Verse 25a is the answer to Paul's cry. Why do you think Paul did not give more *specifics* in the answer? _____

APPLICATIONS

1. Which force is stronger in Paul's experience: external law or indwelling sin?

_____

What does this tell you about the inadequacy of the Law to save? _____

2. Identify yourself with Paul at 7:24, and in your own words describe your basic spiritual needs.

_____

_____

_____

_____

How does Jesus fulfill those needs for you?

_____

_____

Why not share your testimony with a Christian friend this week?

Summary of Passage

Even the Christian who recognizes that God's Law is good has a conflict going on in his heart. He wants to do good, for he learns this from the Law. But he does the very opposite—evil. So he serves the Law of God with his mind, but the law of sin with the flesh.

There is only one solution to this conflict of laws in a Christian's daily walk: deliverance through Jesus Christ his Lord.

Memory Verses   7:24-25a

Looking Ahead

Paul will show specifically how Christ is the all-sufficient answer to the needs of the troubled Christian described in this unit.

SETTING The answer to Paul's cry for deliverance is Christ Jesus (7:24-25). This passage discusses the answer in detail, showing the blessed ministries of Christ and also those of God and the Spirit.

Book of Romans: GOD'S SALVATION FOR SINNEI

P R O L O G U E	NEED OF SALVATION	WAY OF SALVATION	LIFE OF SALVATION	SCOPE OF SALVATION	SERVICES OF SALVATION	E P I L O G U E
		DOCTRINAL			PRACTICAL	
	GOD'S POWER	GOD'S GRACE	GOD'S HOLINESS	GOD'S SOVEREIGNTY	GOD'S GLORY	
1:1	1:18	3:21	6:1	9:1	12:1	15:

BLESSINGS IN CHRIST JESUS

1 There is therefore now
   NO CONDEMNATION for those
      who are IN CHRIST JESUS.
2 For the law of the **Spirit of life** in Christ Jesus
      has set you free
   from the law of **sin** and of **death**.
3 For what the Law could not do,
   weak as it was through the flesh,
         God did:
   sending His own Son
      (1) in the likeness of sinful flesh
   and
      (2) as an **offering for sin**
   He **condemned sin** in the flesh,
4 in order that the requirement of the Law
   might be fulfilled in us,
      who do not walk according to the flesh,
            but according to the Spirit.

NO CONDEMNATION

5   For those who are according to the flesh
      set their **MINDS** on the things of the **flesh**,
   but   those who are according to the **Spirit**,
                  the things of the **Spirit**,
6 For the **MIND** set on the flesh is DEATH.
   but the **MIND** set on the Spirit is LIFE AND PEACE,
7 because the mind set on the flesh
               is **hostile toward GOD**;
   for it does not subject itself to the LAW OF GOD,
   for it is **not even able** to do so;
8 and those who are **in the flesh** cannot PLEASE GOD.

LIFE AND PEACE

9 However, you are not in the **flesh**
               but in the **Spirit**,
   if indeed the Spirit of God **dwells in you**.
   But if anyone does not have the SPIRIT OF CHRIST,
            he does not belong to Him.
10 And if CHRIST IS IN YOU,
   though the body is **dead** because of **sin**,
   yet the spirit is **alive** because of RIGHTEOUSNESS.
11 But if the SPIRIT OF HIM who raised Jesus
               from the dead
   DWELLS IN YOU,
   He who **raised Christ Jesus** from the dead
   will also **give life** to your mortal bodies
      through His Spirit who INDWELLS YOU.

INDWELLINGS

12 So then, **brethren**, we are **under obligation**,
   not to the flesh—
13 for if you are living according to the **flesh**,
            YOU MUST DIE;
   but if **by the Spirit** you are putting to **death**
      the deeds of the body, YOU WILL LIVE.
14 For all who are being **led** by the **Spirit of God**,
            these are SONS OF GOD.
15 For you have not received a spirit of **slavery**
            leading to **fear** again,
   but you have received a spirit of **adoption** as sons
      by which we cry out, "Abba! Father!"
16 The **Spirit Himself** bears witness with **our spirit**
            that we are CHILDREN OF GOD,
17 and if children, heirs also,
   (1) heirs of God and (2) fellow-heirs with Christ,
      if indeed we **suffer with Him** in order that
         we may also be GLORIFIED WITH HIM.

SONSHIP AND INHERITANCE

OBSERVATIONS

Key Words and Phrases

8:1 ___ "no condemnation" _____

2 _____

5 _____

10 _____

11 _____

13 _____

14 _____

17 _____

others: _____
_____

Segment Survey

This is a long segment of four paragraphs, teaching many wonderful truths about the believer's blessings in Christ Jesus. Before you analyze it paragraph by paragraph, read the whole segment twice, and observe the various key repeated words and phrases.

Compare the first verse with the concluding line.

_____
_____

Read each paragraph, and observe the reasons for each part of the outline shown:

> NO CONDEMNATION
> LIFE AND PEACE
> INDWELLINGS
> SONSHIP AND INHERITANCE

Paragraph Analysis

8:1-4

Record what this passage teaches about these:

a. solution to the Law's weakness:

_____
_____

b. solution to the power of the law of sin and deatl

_____
_____

8:5-8

1. How is the phrase "mind set" a key to this paragraph? _____

_____

2. What part does the Spirit play in this mind set

_____
_____
_____

60

8:9-11
What are the references to each Person of the Trinity?

GOD _____

_____

SPIRIT _____

_____

CHRIST _____

_____

8:12-17
1. What are the believer's obligations?

_____

_____

2. What are his blessings and privileges?

_____

_____

_____

_____

3. Compare the last line of the paragraph with the resurrection mentioned in verse 11.

_____

_____

Related Verses

Col. 3:5 _____

_____

Gal. 4:5 _____

_____

Eph. 1:5,14 _____

_____

Heb. 2:9,10 _____

_____

1 Cor. 3:16 _____

_____

Mark 14:36 _____

_____

2 Tim. 2:11-13 _____

_____

INTERPRETATIONS

1. "No condemnation" (8:1). Interpret verse 1 in light of:

a. what Paul has already written:

_____

_____

_____

b. work of the Spirit (v. 2) (TBS#3)

_____

c. work of Father and Son (vv. 3,4)

_____

_____

2. In your own words, write what is meant by these:

flesh mind set: _____

_____

Spirit mind set: _____

3. What do these indwellings mean (vv. 9-11):

Spirit in you: _____

_____

Christ in you: _____

4. "Adoption as sons" (8:15). When a sinner is saved, he comes into the family of God as a child. At the same time his status in the family is that of adoption, with all the privileges of an adult son.

5. "Fellow-heirs with Christ" (8:17). The inheritance is glory, but it also includes suffering.

APPLICATIONS

1. Chapter 8 is a key New Testament chapter about the Holy Spirit. List the practical help the Spirit gives to the Christian. (TBS#3)

_____

_____

_____

_____

_____

2. What *encouragement* do you find in this passage, concerning the conflict of the old and new natures in you?

_____

_____

_____

_____

Summary of Passage

The believer in Christ Jesus has many blessings and much help in his daily walk. He is not a condemned sinner. The indwelling Father, Son and Spirit keep him from sin's controlling power, and he enjoys life and all the privileges of being a child of God and fellow-heir with Christ.

Memory Verses   8:16-17
Looking Ahead

Paul will expand on the subject of suffering in the Christian life, which he introduced at 8:17.

SETTING At 8:17 Paul had written that the believer, as a fellow-heir of Christ, is in the fellowship of Christ's sufferings. Now he expands on this important truth.

Book of Romans: GOD'S SALVATION FOR SINNER

P R O L O G U E	NEED OF SALVATION	WAY OF SALVATION	LIFE OF SALVATION	SCOPE OF SALVATION	SERVICES OF SALVATION	E P I L O G U E
		DOCTRINAL			PRACTICAL	
	GOD'S POWER	GOD'S GRACE	GOD'S HOLINESS	GOD'S SOVEREIGNTY	GOD'S GLORY	
1:1	1:18	3:21	6:1	9:1	12:1	15:1

FRUITS OF SUFFERING

18 For I consider
    that the SUFFERINGS of this present time
        are not worthy to be compared
with the GLORY that is to be revealed to us.
19 For the
    anxious longing of the **creation**
    waits eagerly for
    the revealing of the SONS OF GOD.
20 For the **creation**
      WAS SUBJECTED to **futility**,
      (1) not of its own will,
      (2) but because of **Him**
        who subjected it,
21   IN HOPE that the **creation** itself also
    WILL BE SET FREE
        from its **slavery** to **corruption**
    into the **freedom**
      of the GLORY
      of the CHILDREN OF GOD.

GLORY

22 For we know
    that the **whole creation**
    GROANS and SUFFERS the pains of childbirth
      together until now.
23 And not only this,
    but also we ourselves,
    having the FIRSTFRUITS of the SPIRIT,
      even we ourselves
    GROAN within ourselves,
    waiting eagerly for our ADOPTION AS SONS,
      the REDEMPTION of OUR BODY.
24 For IN HOPE we have been **SAVED**,
    but hope that is SEEN is not hope;
    for why does one also hope for what he sees?
25 But if we HOPE for what we do **not** see,
    with PERSEVERANCE
    we **wait eagerly** for it.

BODY-REDEMPTION

26 And in the same way
    the SPIRIT also **helps our weakness**;
    for we do not know
      HOW TO PRAY as we should,
    but the SPIRIT HIMSELF
      intercedes for us
      with GROANINGS too deep for words;
27 and He who **searches the hearts**
      knows what the **mind of the SPIRIT** is,
    because He **intercedes** for the SAINTS
      according to the WILL of GOD.

INTERCESSION

OBSERVATIONS

Key Words and Phrases

8:18 "sufferings" _____
  19 _____
  21 _____
  22 _____
  23 _____
  24 _____
  26 _____

    27 _____
others: _____
_____

Segment Survey

The segment has three paragraphs, each written in a similar pattern. What subject is common to all three? _____
_____

Observe how the negative references (e.g. "sufferings") appear in the first lines of each paragraph, leading to the positive toward the end.

Note the outline on the textual re-creation chart. Try arriving at another outline of the paragraphs.

Paragraph Analysis

8:18-21

1. Compare the beginning and end of the paragraph. _____
_____

2. How does Paul measure suffering and glory, in verse 18? _____
_____

3. Where and when did suffering begin? _____

4. Whose will the glory be (8:21)? _____
_____

8:22-25

1. Who are the "we ourselves" of verse 23? _____

2. What kind of groaning is meant, according to verse 23? _____

3. What is suggested by the words "waiting eagerly" (8:23)? _____

Where else in the paragraph do these words appear? _____

4. What is the key repeated word of verses 24-25? _____

Why do you think Paul introduces this here? _____

8:26-27

1. Does Paul identify any weakness (v. 26)? If not, what may he have in mind?

_____

_____

2. How does the Spirit intercede (vv. 26,27)?

_____

_____

_____

Why should that intercession be totally

efficient?_____

_____

Related Verses

Gen. 3:17-19_____

_____

Rev. 21:1_____

_____

2 Cor. 1:3-11_____

_____

2 Cor. 4:17 _____

_____

2 Cor. 5:1-10_____

_____

Heb. 7:25 _____

_____

2 Peter 3:13_____

_____

INTERPRETATIONS

1. "The creation was subjected to futility" (8:20). When Adam and Eve sinned, God placed a curse on the human race (Gen. 3:17-19). He also cursed all His other creations below the human level. At the new creation in the end-times (Rev. 21:1), a restoration of creation will be seen (8:21). From that time on, for all eternity, it will be glory for the children of God (8:21).

2. "Redemption of our body" (8:23). Our present bodies still have limitations and flaws, get sick and die, but our resurrection body will be perfect. The "redemption of our body" refers to the event of our receiving such a body.

3. "Having the firstfruits of the Spirit" (8:23). Believers now have the Holy Spirit. This is a sample ("firstfruits") of the full harvest to be reaped when our bodies are made perfect and new ("redemption of our body").

4. Does Paul mention any condition which the believer must meet to receive the help of the Spirit's intercession (8:26-27)? Explain. Also, what does the phrase "according to the will of God" (v. 27) mean?

APPLICATIONS

1. The sufferings of 8:18 are the kind we share with Christ (8:17). Write down some examples of these. Are you experiencing any of these? How does the hope of glory uphold the Christian in such suffering?

_____

_____

_____

_____

_____

2. Do you know of a Christian who is in severe bodily pain and affliction, having a terminal illness? How can you minister hope to such a

believer?_____

_____

_____

_____

_____

Remember also the interceding ministry of the Spirit for such afflictions (8:26-27)!

Summary of Passage

Our sufferings with Christ are minor compared to the glory we'll see in heaven. And these frail bodies, appointed to die, will one day be made perfect. We can count on that hope! In the meantime, there is a solution for every weakness. We don't know how to pray about our weaknesses as we should, but the Holy Spirit intercedes for us, and God hears Him!

A Memory Verse   8:26

Looking Ahead

Paul concludes this "Christian living" section of his letter by showing the many ways that "God is for us."

SETTING Chapter 8 is the last of the three chapters on the *life* of salvation. (See survey chart.) The passage of this unit concludes on the high note of showing how God makes everything work together for His children's good.

Book of Romans: GOD'S SALVATION FOR SINNER

P R O L O G U E	NEED OF SALVATION	WAY OF SALVATION	LIFE OF SALVATION	SCOPE OF SALVATION	SERVICES OF SALVATION	E P I L O G U E
			DOCTRINAL		PRACTICAL	
	GOD'S POWER	GOD'S GRACE	GOD'S HOLINESS	GOD'S SOVEREIGNTY	GOD'S GLORY	
1:1	1:18	3:21	6:1	9:1	12:1	15:1

OBSERVATIONS
Key Words and Phrases

8:28 "for good" _____

29 _____

30 _____

31 _____

33 _____

35 _____

37 _____

39 _____

others: _____

Segment Survey

The segment has three paragraphs. Read it a few times. Who is the most active person in this segment? _____

Note how God and His Son are referred to in each paragraph.

Identify the kind of problem and need in each paragraph. Record this on the textual re-creation chart.

Note the questions which begin with the word "Who." Look for any progression.

Paragraph Analysis
8:28-30
1. What do you consider the key phrase of verse 28? _____

2. What are the two conditions for receiving the help of verse 28? _____

In which is God object, and in which is He subject? _____

3. Record the list of God's ministries (8:29-30). Also, record any progression which you may see in the list. _____

GOD IS FOR US

28 And **we know** that
  GOD causes all things
            to work together **for good**
  to those (1) WHO LOVE GOD,
  to those (2) WHO ARE CALLED
            according to **His purpose**.
29 For WHOM He FOREKNEW,
      He also PREDESTINED
  to become **conformed** to the image of His Son,
            that He might be
    the first-born among many brethren;
30 and WHOM He PREDESTINED,
    these He also CALLED;
  and WHOM He CALLED,
    these He also JUSTIFIED;
  and WHOM HE JUSTIFIED,
    these He also GLORIFIED.

(NO BREAKDOWN)

31 **What then** shall we say to these things?
        If GOD IS FOR US,
        who is against us?
32 He who
  (1) did not spare **His own Son,**
  but
  (2) delivered Him up **for us all,**
  how will He not **also**
        with Him
        freely give us all things?
33 Who will bring a CHARGE against GOD'S ELECT?
      ——→ God is the one who justifies;
34 and who is the one who CONDEMNS?
      ——→ CHRIST JESUS is He who
  (1) **died,**
  (2) yes, rather who was **raised,**
  (3) who is **at the right hand** of God,
  (4) who also **intercedes** for us.

(NO CHARGES)

35 Who shall separate us
        from the LOVE of CHRIST?
  Shall tribulation, or distress, or persecution,
    or famine, or nakedness,
    or peril, or sword?
36 Just as it is written,
  "For Thy sake we are being put to death
    all day long;   [Ps. 44:22]
  We were considered as SHEEP
            to be SLAUGHTERED."
37 But in **all these things**
  we
        **OVERWHELMINGLY CONQUER
        THROUGH HIM**
            who loved us.
38 For I am **convinced** that
  neither death, nor life,
    nor angels, nor principalities,
    nor things present, nor things to come,
  nor powers,
39 nor height, nor depth.
  nor any other created thing,
  shall be able
    to separate us
        from the LOVE of GOD,
          which is in CHRIST JESUS OUR LORD.

(NO SEPARATION)

8:31-34

1. What is the key phrase of verse 31?

_____

2. What help is promised in verse 32?

_____

How is it measured?_____

_____

3. What are the two problem situations of verses 33-34, and what is God's provision in each case?

_____

_____

_____

8:35-39

1. What is the basic problem situation of verses 35-36?_____

_____

How is this problem further described in verses 38-39?_____

_____

How does the central verse (v. 37) relate to its surroundings?_____

_____

2. Paul assures us that "we overwhelmingly conquer" in these threats (8:37). But how does this happen?

_____

_____

_____

Related Verses

1 Cor. 8:3_____

_____

1 Cor. 15:24-28 _____

_____

1 Cor. 15:49_____

_____

2 Cor. 3:18 _____

_____

Eph. 1:4-14_____

_____

Eph. 1:20-23_____

_____

Col. 1:15 _____

_____

1 John 3:2_____

_____

INTERPRETATIONS

1. "Those who love God" (8:28). Those who truly love God are believers who are the called ones, foreknown, predestined, justified and glorified. This love is not mere sentimental feeling.

2. "Predestined" (8:29). Consider this paraphrase. "Whom He knew beforehand, He decided upon beforehand to be conformed...."

3. "First-born" (8:29). Christ is the highest in rank and position among His brothers, the host of believers.

4. "Glorified" (8:30). The believer's glorification is yet future. All the other ministries of 8:29-30 are already the believer's experience.

5. "Love of Christ" (8:35). Is this Christ's love toward us, or our love toward Christ?

_____

_____

6. What variety do you see in the listed things of 8:38? Why do you think Paul used such a wide variety?_____

_____

APPLICATIONS

1. What is your main goal in life?

_____

_____

After you have written your answer, compare it with goals brought out in 8:29 and 1 John 3:2.

2. What do the truths of 8:28-30 assure you, as to your own personal life and destiny?

_____

_____

How should this affect your attitudes and spirit in everyday living?_____

_____

3. How can Christians be victorious in the experience of verses 35-39? What has been your personal experience?_____

_____

Summary of Passage

We Christians have all the help we need in the difficult experiences of life. God works everything for good, so that His full purposes for us may be accomplished. No foe can defeat us spiritually, for He is for us. And nothing can separate us from His love and the love of His Son.

A Memory Verse   8:28

Looking Ahead

Paul will begin to write especially about the salvation of Jews, recalling what he had written in the opening lines (1:16) that salvation is for *both* Jew and Gentile.

SCOPE OF SALVATION
9:1–11:36

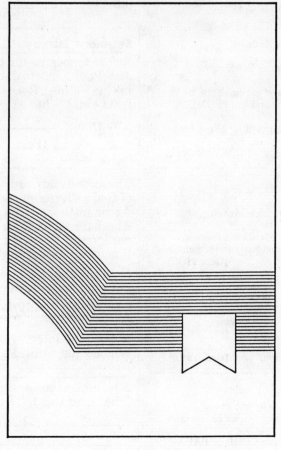

SETTING Paul has been teaching such key salvation doctrines as justification, sanctification and glorification. Now we might expect him to apply those doctrines by way of practical commands. But before he does that, he has more to say about salvation of Jews. This is the subject of the next three chapters (ch. 9: ISRAEL'S PAST; ch. 10: ISRAEL'S PRESENT; ch. 11: ISRAEL'S FUTURE). Note on the survey chart that God's *sovereignty* is a prominent attribute here.

GOD'S SOVEREIGN PURPOSES

1 I am telling the truth **in Christ**,
I am not lying,
my conscience bearing me witness
in the HOLY SPIRIT,
2 that I have GREAT SORROW
and UNCEASING GRIEF in my heart.
3 For I could wish
that **I myself** were ACCURSED,
SEPARATED from Christ
for the sake of
my brethren,
my kinsmen according to the flesh,
4 who are ISRAELITES,
to whom belongs the adoption as SONS
and the GLORY
and the COVENANTS and giving of the LAW
and the TEMPLE service and the PROMISES,
5 whose are the FATHERS, and
from whom is THE CHRIST according to the flesh,
who is **over all**,
GOD BLESSED FOREVER. Amen.

PAUL'S GRIEF

6 But it is not as though
the WORD OF GOD has failed.
For they are not all **Israel**
who are descended from **Israel**;
7 Neither are they all CHILDREN
because they are Abraham's descendants,
but: "Through **Isaac** your descendants will be named."
[Gen. 21:12]
8 **That is,**
it is not the children of the FLESH
who are CHILDREN OF GOD,
but the children of the PROMISE
are regarded as descendants.
9 For this is a word of promise:
"At this time I will come,
and Sarah shall have a son." [Gen. 18:10]

ISAAC CHOSEN

10 And not only this,
but there was Rebekah also,
when she had conceived twins by one man,
our father **Isaac**;
11 for though the twins were not yet born,
and had not done anything GOOD or BAD,
in order that
GOD'S PURPOSE
according to HIS CHOICE
MIGHT STAND,
not because of WORKS,
but because of HIM WHO CALLS,
12 it was said to her,
"The **older** will serve the **younger**." [Gen. 25:23]
13 Just as it is written,
"**Jacob** I loved, but **Esau** I hated." [Mal. 1:2 f.]

JACOB CHOSEN

Book of Romans: GOD'S SALVATION FOR SINNER[S]

PROLOGUE	NEED OF SALVATION	WAY OF SALVATION	LIFE OF SALVATION	SCOPE OF SALVATION	SERVICES OF SALVATION	EPILOGUE
	DOCTRINAL				PRACTICAL	
	GOD'S POWER	GOD'S GRACE	GOD'S HOLINESS	GOD'S SOVEREIGNTY	GOD'S GLORY	
1:1	1:18	3:21	6:1	9:1	12:1	15:14

OBSERVATIONS

Key Words and Phrases

9:2 "great sorrow" __________
3 __________
4 __________
5 __________
6 __________
7 __________
10 __________
11 __________
others: __________

Segment Survey

Before he begins his three-chapter essay on the Jew, Paul wants to unburden his heart by sharing his feelings. Read the first paragraph. What is its tone? What are the four last words of the paragraph? __________

The second and third paragraphs give examples of God's sovereign choices of descendants of Abraham to serve His purposes in the world. Of Abraham's sons, God chose the Isaac line (second paragraph). Of Isaac's sons, God chose the Jacob line (third paragraph).

Note the title assigned to the segment, and the key phrase from which it is taken (v. 11).

Paragraph Analysis

9:1-5

1. Note the intensity of the solemn oath (v. 1). Why do you think Paul was so emphatic?

2. Note also the heaviness of Paul's heart-burden. What does this tell you about Paul?

3. How was Paul related to the Israelites (v. 3)?

4. In one sentence describe the privileges and honors of the Israelites. __________

5. Does this opening paragraph explicitly identify the problem? If not, where in the segment is that first mentioned? __________

9:6-9

1. Verse 6 is a key verse in the entire segment. The second half of the verse states the problem of the segment, which Paul had not identified in the first paragraph. What is the problem?

_____

Why does Paul write verse 6a?

_____

2. After saying that "they are not all Israel who are descended from Israel" (9:6b), Paul cites two examples. Which is the example in this paragraph?_____

9:10-13

1. The key phrase of absolute divine sovereignty is in verse 11. What is it?

_____

2. What example does Paul cite in this paragraph?_____

3. What are God's choices based upon, according to 9:11b?_____

What are they *not* based upon?

_____

Related Verses

Gen. 12:1-3_____

Ex. 4:22 _____

Ex. 16:10 _____

Isa. 52:13–53:12_____

Rom. 2:28 ff._____

Gal. 4:22-31_____

Eph. 2:12 _____

INTERPRETATIONS

1. "From whom is the Christ according to the flesh" (9:5). What does this refer to?

_____

2. Israelites who are related to Abraham only as "children of the flesh" (9:8—blood relatives) are not true Jews, but only Jews outwardly (2:28-29). There is a difference between carnal sonship and spiritual sonship. And the condition of spiritual sonship is faith, not heredity. So "flesh" (v. 8) and "works" (v. 11) are ruled out when determining who the people of God are.

3. "Esau I hated" (9:13). In the context of the passage from which this is quoted (Mal. 1:2-3), Edom and Esau are nations—Israel and Edom. The contrasting verbs "loved" and "hated" are as far apart as they can be, which is the exaggeration intended.

APPLICATIONS

1. Paul was grieving with great sorrow over the spiritual condition of his Jewish brethren, yet he did not lose sight of "God blessed forever" (9:5). What do you learn from this? Do you have unsaved friends and loved ones for whose salvation you have been praying long? Do you have peace of heart about who God is and about His answers to your prayers?

_____
_____
_____

2. What spiritual help comes to you when you meditate on the sovereignty of God: who He is, and that His purposes stand according to *His* choice?_____
How does this affect your witnessing to unsaved souls? Discuss this with your group.

Summary of Passage

Paul knows that many of his Jewish friends and "kinsmen" are not children of God, because they are depending on works to save them, not faith. So he grieves with a heavy heart over them.

The apostle shows that blessings and privileges have come to Israelites, but only to those who are children of God by faith. Ever since Abraham, the children of God's promises have been the ones He called, not those striving to be accepted by works.

Memory Verses   9:2,3
Looking Ahead

Paul will say more about God's sovereignty in the picture of the Potter.

SETTING In the last segment Paul introduced God's sovereign purposes as determining in history the mission of the true children of His promise. Now he writes more about this sovereign God.

THE POTTER AND THE CLAY

14 What shall we say?
There is no INJUSTICE with God,
is there?
May it never be!
15 For He says to MOSES,
"I will have MERCY ON WHOM I HAVE MERCY,
and I will have COMPASSION
ON WHOM I HAVE COMPASSION."   [Ex. 33:19]
16 So then
it does **not depend** on
(1) the MAN who WILLS
or
(2) the MAN who RUNS,
but on GOD WHO HAS MERCY.

[margin: MOSES]

17 For the Scripture says to PHARAOH,
"For this VERY PURPOSE
I raised you up,
(1) to DEMONSTRATE MY POWER IN YOU, and
(2) that MY NAME might be PROCLAIMED
throughout the **whole earth**." [Ex. 9:16]
18 So then
(1) He has MERCY on whom HE DESIRES, and
(2) He HARDENS whom HE DESIRES.

[margin: PHARAOH]

19 You will say to me then,
"Why does He still find fault?
For who resists His will?"
20 On the contrary,
who are you, O man,
who **answers back to God?**
The thing molded will not say to the molder,
"Why did you **make me like this**,"
will it?
21 Or does not the POTTER
have a RIGHT OVER THE CLAY,
to make from the **same lump**
(1) one vessel for **honorable** use, and
(2) another for **common** use?

[margin: CLAY]

OBSERVATIONS

Key Words and Phrases

9:14 "injustice"
15
16
17
18
19
20
21

others:

Book of Romans: GOD'S SALVATION FOR SINNER

P R O L O G U E	NEED OF SALVATION	WAY OF SALVATION	LIFE OF SALVATION	SCOPE OF SALVATION	SERVICES OF SALVATION	E P I L O G U E
	DOCTRINAL				PRACTICAL	
	GOD'S POWER	GOD'S GRACE	GOD'S HOLINESS	GOD'S SOVEREIGNTY	GOD'S GLORY	
1:1	1:18	3:21	6:1	9:1	12:1	15:

Segment Survey

How does the opening verse relate to the preceding passage?

Read the three paragraphs, and observe the key characters or objects in each.

What is similar about the concluding verses of each paragraph?

Paragraph Analysis

9:14-16
1. The first question of verse 14 indicates that Paul is answering objections over what he has just discussed (e.g. 9:11). Write down what the objectors may have been saying.

2. What attribute of God must be fully recognized in all discussions of God's sovereign choices (9:14)?

3. Read Exodus 33:12-19. Observe the context of 33:19 which Paul quotes in Romans 9:15. Did Moses show any desire and effort in his conversations with God? If so, what?

Read Romans 9:16. (NIV translation: "It does not...depend on man's desire or effort.)

9:17-18
1. Read Exodus 9:13-17. Observe the context of Exodus 9:16, which Paul quotes in Romans 9:17.
2. What does this example of God's using Pharaoh add to the illustration of His using Moses (vv. 14-16)?

3. What key word of verse 18 is the clue to what determines God's choices?

9:19-21

1. How do the preceding two paragraphs bring on the questions of verse 19?

_____

2. In your own words, what is Paul's reply?

_____

3. How does the phrase, "for common use" (v. 21), enlarge the total picture of the sovereignty of God's choices?_____

Related Verses

Ex. 4:21_____

Ex. 10:1,2_____

Isa. 45:9,10_____

Isa. 64:8_____

Eph. 2:8_____

Rom. 11:7,25 _____
_____

INTERPRETATIONS

1. Why does Paul raise the question about *injustice* with God at the opening of this segment (v. 14)? _____

2. What do the following words, taken from this passage, have to do with the sovereignty of God?

"I will" (9:15)_____

"depend on" (9:16)_____

"purpose" (9:17) _____

"desires" (9:18) _____

"right" (9:21)_____

3. What things are attributed to God in this passage? (e.g. power, v. 17)?

_____
_____
_____

APPLICATIONS

Three realms of God's sovereign workings are represented by the three paragraphs:

(1) first paragraph: SALVATION ◆ "mercy"
(2) second paragraph: RULERSHIP ◆ "power"
(3) third paragraph: CREATION ◆❙ "make"

Make a list of applications for each topic. For example, in the area of SALVATION, how should Christians show their gratitude to Him for His mercy, in worship and in service?

_____
_____
_____
_____
_____
_____
_____
_____
_____
_____
_____
_____

Summary of Passage

God remains wholly just in all His sovereign ways. Whom He saves depends on Himself who is merciful. Whom He chooses to demonstrate His power, comes of His own purposes. And how He wants to use each person He has created is entirely His right.

A Memory Verse   9:21

Looking Ahead

Paul will illustrate the truth of God's sovereignty in the area of salvation.

SETTING This segment concludes Paul's essay (9:6-29) on the absolute sovereignty of God with relation to Israel's past.

The next section (9:30–10:21) focuses on the Jews' present responsibility, and on why they are a rejected people.

OBJECTS OF MERCY

22   What if God,
       although WILLING
     (1) to DEMONSTRATE HIS WRATH and
     (2) to MAKE HIS POWER KNOWN,
         endured with **much patience**
       vessels of WRATH prepared for DESTRUCTION?
23 And He did so in order that
           He might MAKE KNOWN
      the riches of HIS GLORY
    upon vessels of MERCY,
         which He prepared beforehand for GLORY,
24   even us,
     whom He also CALLED,
       not from among Jews only,
     but also from among Gentiles.
25 As He says also in Hosea,
   "I will **call** those who were NOT MY PEOPLE,
                'MY PEOPLE.'
       and her who was NOT BELOVED,
            'BELOVED.'" [Hos. 2:23]
26 "And it shall be that
    in the place where it was said to them,
      'You are NOT MY PEOPLE,'
    there they shall be called
      SONS OF THE LIVING GOD."   [Hos. 1:10]

(margin: SAVED JEWS AND GENTILES)

27 And Isaiah cries out concerning ISRAEL,
   "Though the **number** of the children of ISRAEL
      be as the **sand of the sea**,
    it is the REMNANT that will be SAVED;
                [Isa. 10:22]
28 For the Lord will **execute His Word**
           upon the **earth**,
       thoroughly and **quickly**."   [Isa. 10:23]
29 And just as Isaiah foretold,
   "Except the **Lord of Sabaoth**
       had **left to us** A POSTERITY,
   (1) We would have become as Sodom,
   (2) and would have resembled Gomorrah."   [Isa. 1:9]

(margin: SAVED REMNANT)

OBSERVATIONS

Key Words and Phrases

9:22   "vessels of wrath" _____

    23 _____

    24 _____

    25 _____

    26 _____

    27 _____

    27 _____

    29 _____

others: _____

_____

Book of Romans: GOD'S SALVATION FOR SINNER

P R O L O G U E	NEED OF SALVATION	WAY OF SALVATION	LIFE OF SALVATION	SCOPE OF SALVATION	SERVICES OF SALVATION	E P I L O G U E
			DOCTRINAL		PRACTICAL	
	GOD'S POWER	GOD'S GRACE	GOD'S HOLINESS	GOD'S SOVEREIGNTY	GOD'S GLORY	
1:1	1:18	3:21	6:1	9:1	12:1	15:

Segment Survey

Read the two paragraphs of the segment. Which paragraph is about Jews only?

_____

Observe the outline shown on the chart.

Note every reference (word or phrase) to a believer.

Paragraph Analysis

9:22-26

1. What two vessels (NIV—"objects") does Paul write about here? _____

_____

How would you identify them? (Note the clue in verse 24a.) _____

2. Compare this *Living Bible* paraphrase with the NASB text of verses 22-24:

"Does not God have a perfect right to show his fury and power against those who are fit only for destruction, those he has been patient with for all this time? And he has a right to take others such as ourselves, who have been made for pouring the riches of his glory into, whether we are Jews or Gentile, and to be kind to us so that everyone can see how very great his glory is."

3. What do verses 25 and 26 teach about God's election of Gentiles for salvation?

_____

_____

In what ways are saved Gentiles referred to here?

_____

_____

_____

_____

9:27-29

1. What do these verses teach about how many Jews will be saved for eternity?

_____

_____

2. What two words identify these saved Jews?

_____

_____

Related Verses

Prov. 16:4 _____

_____

Amos 4:11 _____

Acts 9:15_____

Rom. 2:4_____

Rom. 3:29_____

Rom. 8:28,29 _____

Rom. 11:5_____

INTERPRETATIONS

1. You have read the *Living Bible* paraphrase of verses 22-24. Now read the NASB text again, and think how the meaning of the three verses could be expressed in one long sentence. Then in your own words write that sentence.

_____

_____

_____

2. Refer to the survey chart of Romans, and note that the section beginning at 9:1 is identified as SCOPE OF SALVATION. What is that scope, according to the passage of this unit?

_____

_____

3. Read the Hosea passages noted in brackets to see the historical setting of the quotes.
4. The "sons of Israel" (9:27) are the blood descendants of Abraham. The faith descendants, true Israel, are the saved remnant.
5. Verse 28 is about future judgment. NIV translates, "For the Lord will carry out his sentence on earth with speed and finality."

APPLICATIONS

1. What do you learn here about the Lord's patience and longsuffering before sending judgment, and His love in calling sinners to His family? _____

_____

_____

_____

_____

_____

_____

_____

_____

_____

_____

How can you share this truth with an unsaved person to whom you are witnessing Christ?

_____

_____

_____

_____

_____

_____

_____

_____

_____

_____

_____

_____

2. What is the sobering truth in verse 28 about God's judgment? How would you use this in witnessing to a lost soul, whether Jew or Gentile? Discuss this with your group. (TBS#7)

Summary of Passage

God is patient and longsuffering toward sinners who reject Him, but their judgment is sure. Those whom He sovereignly calls to Himself to be His children, of Jews *and* Gentiles, know of His power and wrath against unbelievers. They also know that His calling of them is all of mercy.

The blood descendants of Abraham are many, but the saved ones are a remnant of those.

A Memory Verse   9:27
Looking Ahead

Paul will explain why some Gentiles are saved and some Jews are not saved.

SETTING In the previous segment of 9:26-29 Paul has taught the truth of God's sovereignty, especially as it involves the Jews' salvation. He has surveyed Israel's past. Beginning with this segment he focuses on the present, which includes the entire Church Age.

Book of Romans: GOD'S SALVATION FOR SINNER

P R O L O G U E	NEED OF SALVATION	WAY OF SALVATION	LIFE OF SALVATION	SCOPE OF SALVATION	SERVICES OF SALVATION	E P I L O G U E
		DOCTRINAL			PRACTICAL	
	GOD'S POWER	GOD'S GRACE	GOD'S HOLINESS	GOD'S SOVEREIGNTY	GOD'S GLORY	
1:1	1:18	3:21	6:1	9:1	12:1	15:

WRONG KIND OF ZEAL

9:30 What shall we say then?
That
    (1) GENTILES,
      who did not **pursue righteousness,**
      attained righteousness,
    even the **righteousness** which is BY **FAITH;**
31 but
    (2) Israel,
          pursuing a law of **righteousness,**
          did not arrive at that law.
32 WHY?
    Because they did **not pursue** it BY **FAITH,**
      but as it were by **works.**
    They **stumbled** over the STUMBLING STONE,
33 just as it is written,
    "Behold, I lay in Zion
      (1) a stone of **stumbling** and
      (2) a rock of offense,   [Isa. 28:16]
    And he who **BELIEVES IN HIM**
             will not be disappointed."

NO FAITH

10:1 Brethren,
      (1) my **heart's desire** and
      (2) my **prayer to God**
  for them is FOR THEIR SALVATION.
2 For I bear them witness that
        they have a ZEAL FOR GOD,
      but not in accordance with KNOWLEDGE.
3 For
    (1) not KNOWING about GOD'S RIGHTEOUSNESS, and
    (2) seeking to **establish their own,**
    they did **not subject themselves**
        to the RIGHTEOUSNESS OF GOD.

NO KNOWLEDGE

OBSERVATIONS

Key Words and Phrases

9:30 "Gentiles" _____

  30 _____

  31 _____

  31 _____

  32 _____

10:1 _____

  2 _____

  3 _____

others: _____

_____

Segment Survey

1. Who is the segment about, mainly?

_____

_____

_____

2. Is Christ mentioned by name? If not, how is He referred to? _____

_____

3. What is the prominent pronoun in the second paragraph? To whom does it refer?

_____

4. Note the outline: NO FAITH; NO KNOWLEDGE. Try to make your own outline, and record it on the chart.

Paragraph Analysis

9:30-33

1. How many times does the word "righteousness" appear in the paragraph? _____
Compare this with the appearances in the second paragraph. _____

_____

_____

2. What three things are written about righteousness and the Gentile in verse 9:30?

(1) _____

(2) _____

(3) _____

What does this suggest about the meaning of this righteousness? _____

_____

3. What did Israel pursue?

_____

Why did they fail to arrive there?

_____

What did they stumble over?

_____

4. Does Paul identify the stumbling stone by name? Whom does the description fit?

_____

5. Note the word "believes" (v. 33). What similar word appears earlier in the paragraph?

_____

10:1-3

1. Compare "their salvation" (10:1) with "arrive at that law" (9:31). _____

_____

_____

_____

2. What did the Jews have (10:2)?

_____

_____

What did they lack?

_____

_____

3. How does verse 3 explain verse 2?

_____

_____

_____

Related Verses

Acts 21:20 _____

_____

Rom. 1:16-17 _____

_____

Rom. 3:21-26 _____

_____

1 Cor. 1:23 _____

_____

Gal. 2:16 _____

_____

Gal. 5:11 _____

_____

Heb. 11:7 _____

_____

James 2:10 _____

_____

INTERPRETATIONS

1. In the early chapters of the epistle (e.g. 1:16-17) Paul had established that salvation for the sinner is given when he receives God's righteousness through faith in Christ. That is faith-righteousness (9:30). The Jews of Paul's day (9:32-33) pursued salvation by works (law-righteousness), but did not arrive at salvation because they did not believe in Jesus (faith-righteousness).

2. Zeal for God (10:2) is good, but only if certain conditions are met. What are these, according to

10:2-3? _____

_____

_____

_____

3. What is the common heart-tone in each of these: "by works" (9:32); "establish their own" (10:3); and "did not subject themselves" (10:3)?

_____

_____

_____

4. "rock of offense" (9:33). Discuss with your group why you think Jesus was an offense to the Jews.

APPLICATIONS

1. Jews are not the only ones who count on works for salvation. You probably know many people in that lost condition. What truths from this passage could you share with an unsaved person who feels he is good enough to get to heaven?

_____

_____

_____

_____

_____

_____

_____

_____

_____

_____

_____

_____

_____

_____

_____

Use these the next time you witness to such a person.

2. What do *desire* and **prayer** (10:1) have to do with witnessing? Examine your own heart concerning this. (TBS#7)

Summary of Passage

Jews are saved the same way Gentiles are saved: by believing in Christ. A Jew may have a zeal for God and a deep desire to be accepted by God, and he may be outwardly righteous, but God's righteousness is imparted to him only when he believes in Christ. God has established this as the only way of salvation, and everyone must subject himself to His way.

A Memory Verse   10:1

Looking Ahead

Paul will show specifically how a person is saved.

SETTING The preceding segment showed that the Jews failed in their pursuit of salvation. In this passage Paul shows how anyone—Jew or Gentile—can be saved.

Book of Romans: GOD'S SALVATION FOR SINNER

P R O L O G U E	NEED OF SALVATION	WAY OF SALVATION	LIFE OF SALVATION	SCOPE OF SALVATION	SERVICES OF SALVATION	E P I L O G U E
		DOCTRINAL			PRACTICAL	
	GOD'S POWER	GOD'S GRACE	GOD'S HOLINESS	GOD'S SOVEREIGNTY	GOD'S GLORY	
1:1	1:18	3:21	6:1	9:1	12:1	15:

SALVATION IS AVAILABLE

4 For CHRIST is the end of the law
      for RIGHTEOUSNESS
        to everyone who BELIEVES.
5 For MOSES writes that
    the man who **practices** the **righteousness**
      which is **based on law**
      shall **live** by that **righteousness.**   [Lev. 18:5]
6 But the RIGHTEOUSNESS based on FAITH
             speaks thus,
  "Do not say in your **heart,**
   'Who will **ascend** into **heaven?'**
  (that is, to **bring CHRIST down),**
7 or 'Who will **descend** into the **abyss?'**
      (that is, to bring CHRIST up from the dead)."
8 But what does it say?
    'The WORD is
      (1) **near** you,
      (2) in your **mouth** and
      (3) in your **heart"**   [Deut. 30:12-14]
  —that is,
    the WORD OF FAITH which we are **preaching,**
9 that if you
    (1) CONFESS with your **mouth**
           JESUS AS LORD, and
    (2) BELIEVE in your **heart**
           that God raised Him from the dead,
  ——▶ YOU SHALL BE SAVED;

SALVATION IS AVAILABLE

10 for with the **heart** man BELIEVES,
         resulting in RIGHTEOUSNESS,
  and with the **mouth** he CONFESSES,
         resulting in SALVATION.
11 For the Scripture says,
   "Whoever BELIEVES in Him
      will not be disappointed."   [Isa. 28:16]
12 For there is **no distinction** between Jew and Greek;
    for the SAME LORD is LORD OF ALL,
        abounding in RICHES
      for ALL who **call upon Him;**
13 for "Whoever
    will **call upon** the NAME of the LORD
      ——▶ WILL BE SAVED."   [Joel 2:32]

INVITATION TO ALL

OBSERVATIONS

Key Words and Phrases

10:4 "righteousness" _____

4 _____

6 _____

8 _____

9 _____

10 _____

12 _____

13 _____

others: _____

_____

Segment Survey

First, relate the opening verse (10:4) to the preceding segment (9:30–10:3), recalling that Christ had not been identified by *name* in that segment.

Compare the last verses of the two paragraphs of this segment.

What is common to each?_____

_____

What is different? _____

_____

Why is the second paragraph identified in the outline as INVITATION TO ALL?

_____

_____

Paragraph Analysis

10:4-9

1. In what verse does this phrase appear: "righteousness...based on law"? _____

_____

Is it possible for anyone to live by that law without breaking it? How does James 2:10 answer this question? _____

_____

Who is the answer to our predicament (10:4)?

_____

2. The remainder of the paragraph is about the "righteousness based on faith" (10:6). What problem of the seeking sinner is illustrated in verses 6 and 7?_____

_____

3. What answer comes back from the faith-righteousness (10:8)?

_____

_____

_____

4. What are the two main points of the "word of faith" (10:8-9)?_____

_____

_____

What are the two key words which are the conditions for being saved? _____

_____

10:10-13

1. Compare verse 10 with verse 9, for likenesses and differences. (Note: verse 10 could be regarded as the concluding verse of the first paragraph.)

2. What words in verses 11-13 teach that the invitation for salvation is for *everyone*?

_____

How are Jews and Gentiles ("Greeks") brought into this discussion? _____

_____

3. What is the one condition for salvation cited in verse 13? _____

_____

Related Verses

Ezek. 20:11,13,21 _____

_____

Matt. 10:32 _____

_____

Luke 12:8 _____

_____

Acts 13:39 _____

_____

Acts 16:31 _____

_____

Rom. 3:22-24 _____

_____

Rom. 3:29 _____

_____

Gal. 3:24 _____

_____

INTERPRETATIONS

1. "End of the law" (10:4). The *New English Bible* translates, "Christ ends the law and brings righteousness for everyone who has faith." Compare Acts 13:39. If a man could keep all the commandments all the time, he would be righteous already. Recall in your earlier studies that Paul has taught that no one is righteous, for all have sinned (3:10,23). The sinner cannot find salvation by trying to keep the law. This is where faith-righteousness comes in.

2. The *Living Bible* paraphrases 10:6-7 this way: "But the salvation that comes through faith says, 'You don't need to search the heavens to find Christ and bring him down to help you,' and 'You don't need to go among the dead to bring Christ back to life again.'"

3. "Confess...believe" (10:9). The conditions for salvation are stated in the New Testament in different but non-contradictory ways, depending on the setting and purpose. Read these passages, and discuss them in your group:

Romans 10:9
Romans 10:10
Acts 16:31
Mark 16:16

APPLICATIONS

Read the entire passage again and record all the happy truths about salvation which Paul brings to our attention. For example, what three promises are made in verses 11-13 to the one who calls upon the Lord?

10:4-9 _____

_____

_____

_____

_____

10:10-13 _____

_____

_____

_____

When you witness to an unsaved soul, be sure to share these happy truths.

Summary of Passage

Christ and the salvation He offers to sinners are not afar off. The salvation comes by faith in Him, and the invitation to believe is to everyone, Jew and non-Jew. Whoever will call upon the name of the Lord, believing with the heart and confessing with the mouth, will be saved.

A Memory Verse   10:9

Looking Ahead

Paul will show that the Jews are without excuse in their unbelief, for the gospel has been universally preached.

SETTING In the preceding passage Paul had shown that salvation is available and the invitation is to all people. Now he shows how the Jews have rejected the glad tidings sent from God.

Book of Romans: GOD'S SALVATION FOR SINNER

P R O L O G U E	NEED OF SALVATION	WAY OF SALVATION	LIFE OF SALVATION	SCOPE OF SALVATION	SERVICES OF SALVATION	E P I L O G U E
			DOCTRINAL		PRACTICAL	
	GOD'S POWER	GOD'S GRACE	GOD'S HOLINESS	GOD'S SOVEREIGNTY	GOD'S GLORY	
1:1	1:18	3:21	6:1	9:1	12:1	15:1

ISRAEL HAS HEARD THE GOSPEL

14 How then
    (1) shall they **CALL** upon **HIM**
          in whom they have NOT BELIEVED? And
    (2) how shall they **BELIEVE in HIM**
          whom they have NOT HEARD? And
    (3) how shall they HEAR WITHOUT a PREACHER? And
15   (4) how shall they PREACH
          UNLESS they are SENT?
  Just as it is written,
    "How **beautiful** are the feet of those
      who bring GLAD TIDINGS
        of GOOD THINGS!"   [Isa. 52:7]

PREACHING

16 However,
    they did not all HEED the GLAD TIDINGS;
  For Isaiah says,
    "Lord, who has BELIEVED our report?" [Isa. 53:1]
17   SO
      (1) FAITH comes from HEARING, and
      (2) HEARING by the WORD OF CHRIST.

RESPONSE

18 But I say,
    surely they have never HEARD, have they?
    Indeed they have:
    "Their VOICE has gone out into ALL the earth,
    And their WORDS to the ENDS of the world."
          [Ps. 19:4]
19 But I say,
    surely ISRAEL did not **KNOW**, did they?
  At the first Moses says,
    "I will make you JEALOUS
      by that which is **not a nation**,
    By a **nation without understanding**
      will I ANGER you."   [Deut. 32:21]
20 And Isaiah is very bold and says,
    "I was FOUND by those who **sought Me NOT**,
    I became MANIFEST to those
      who did **NOT ask** for Me." [Isa. 65:1]
21 But as for ISRAEL he says,
    "**All the day** long
    I have stretched out My hands
      to a **disobedient**
        and **obstinate** people." [Isa. 65:2]

EXAMPLES OF RESPONSE

OBSERVATIONS

Key Words and Phrases

10:14 "call upon Him" _____

  15 _____

  16 _____

  17 _____

  18 _____

  19 _____

  20 _____

  21 _____

others: _____

_____

Segment Survey

The three paragraphs are very different from each other, though the connections are there. Refer to the sequence below as you read the paragraphs. Keep in mind that Paul is answering the unstated arguments of Jews who are excusing their unbelief by contending that the gospel has never reached them.

10:14-15
Preachers *have* been sent to Israel (10:15b).

10:16-17
Not all Jews have heeded the glad tidings.

10:18-21
Jews have heard the redemptive message many times and in many ways (10:18-20). Christ has been longsuffering in His invitations to Israel (10:21).

Paragraph Analysis

10:14-15

1. How is the opening question of 10:14 brought on by 10:13? _____

_____

2. Read Paul's answer in reverse, according to the real *time* sequence (10:14-15):

a. God *has* sent preachers—"how beautiful" are their feet!

b. They have preached the message.

c. The people have heard.

d. They have had the choice of believing.

e. If they had believed, they would have called upon God.

3. What do you observe about the sovereignty of God in 10:14-15? For example, what does it include? _____

_____

_____

What must the sinner do to be saved (10:14a)?

_____

_____

10:16-17

1. What was the response of many Jews to the preaching of glad tidings? _____

_____

_____

2. How is verse 17 a summary of the sequence of verses 14-15? _____

_____

0:18-21

1. Verse 18: How is the question of v. 18a answered? Who is "they," and what is "their voice"?_____

2. Verse 19: The phrase "not a nation" refers to Gentiles. Who is the "I" of Moses' quotation?

_____

How is the question of v. 19a answered?

_____

3. Verse 20: Who is the "I" of Isaiah's quotation?

Who are "those who sought me not"?

_____

_____

4. How does verse 21 summarize the entire segment?_____

_____

_____

Related Verses

Acts 18:5,6_____

Rom. 1:15,16_____

Rom. 11:11-14_____

Gal. 3:2,5_____

Col. 1:6,23_____

Thess. 1:8_____

INTERPRETATIONS

1. In Chapter 9 we observed Israel in the *past*, as God's sovereignly selected nation. Chapter 10 (including the passage of this unit) shows Israel in the *present*, extended the invitation to believe, but rejected by God for their refusal and obstinacy. In Chapter 11 we will see Israel's bright *future*, when God in His mercy restores them when they turn to Him.

2. "The word of Christ" (10:17). Does the context indicate this to be the written or the spoken word? _____

3. The phrases "not a nation" (10:19) and "those who sought me not" (10:20) refer to Gentiles. When the Jews rejected God's invitation for salvation, He gave it to the Gentiles. Paul will write more about this in Chapter 11. For now,

read 11:11. Also read in Acts 13:42–14:7 how Paul had experienced these things about eight years earlier, on his missionary venture.

4. How does the phrase "to the Jew first and also to the Greek" (1:16) relate to the theme of this passage? _____

_____

APPLICATIONS

1. How can this passage help you witness to an unsaved Jew about the gospel of Jesus Christ?

_____

_____

_____

2. How can this passage help you witness to *any* unsaved person? For example, what does it teach about:

God and Christ:_____

_____

_____

How to be saved:_____

_____

_____

3. Pray now that God will lead you to some unsaved person today to whom you can witness.

Summary of Passage

The proclamation of glad tidings of salvation through Christ continues day by day, under God's control. He sends out His witnesses who teach and preach the gospel, and some unsaved souls hear and believe, and call upon the Lord.

The glad tidings were preached to Israel, and when they rejected the message it was given also to Gentiles, to stir up the Jews to jealousy. So the Jews are without excuse. They have had access to the gospel message, and the Lord continues to woo them.

Memory Verses   10:14-15

Looking Ahead

The next unit begins the third and last section in Romans about Jews. Paul will emphasize the truth that God has not rejected His people Israel.

SETTING This passage begins the third and concluding section on Israel.

The picture of Israel looks bright as one looks into the end-times and sees restoration.

ch. 9	ch. 10	ch. 11
PAST	PRESENT	FUTURE
Israel Selected	Israel Rejected	Israel Restored

THE REMNANT OF ISRAEL

1 I say then,
    GOD **has not rejected** HIS PEOPLE,
        has He? May it never be!
    For I too am
        (1) an **Israelite**,
        (2) a descendant of **Abraham**,
        (3) of the tribe of **Benjamin**.
2 GOD **has not rejected**
        HIS PEOPLE whom HE FOREKNEW.
    Or do you not know what the SCRIPTURE SAYS
        in the passage about Elijah,
        how he **pleads with GOD** against ISRAEL?
3 "Lord,
    (1) they have **killed** THY PROPHETS,
    (2) they have **torn down** THINE ALTARS, and
    (3) I alone am left, and
    (4) they are seeking my life."   [1 Kings 19:10,14]
4 But what is the DIVINE RESPONSE to him?
            "I have kept for MYSELF
        seven thousand
        who have not bowed the knee to Baal."
                                [1 Kings 19:18]

5 In the **same way** then,
        there has **also come to be**
            at the present time
            A REMNANT
        according to **GOD'S GRACIOUS CHOICE.**
6 But if it is by **GRACE**,
        it is **no longer**
        on the basis of **WORKS**,
    otherwise **grace is no longer grace.**

7 What then?
        THAT which ISRAEL is seeking for,
        IT HAS NOT OBTAINED,
    but
        those who were CHOSEN **obtained it,**
        and the rest
        were **HARDENED**;
8   just as it is written,
            "GOD gave them a spirit of STUPOR,
            Eyes to see not and
            Ears to hear not,
            Down to **this very day.**"
                        [Isa. 29:10, Deut. 29:4]
9 And David says,
        "Let their **table** become
            (1) a snare and a trap, and
            (2) a stumbling-block and
                a retribution to them,   [Ps. 69:22 ff.]
10 Let their **eyes** be darkened to see not, and
    Bend their **backs** forever."   [Ps. 69:23]

(side labels: IN OLD TESTAMENT TIMES / IN FIRST CENTURY / THE NON-REMNANT)

Book of Romans: GOD'S SALVATION FOR SINNER

P R O L O G U E	NEED OF SALVATION	WAY OF SALVATION	LIFE OF SALVATION	SCOPE OF SALVATION	SERVICES OF SALVATION	E P I L O G U E
	DOCTRINAL				PRACTICAL	
	GOD'S POWER	GOD'S GRACE	GOD'S HOLINESS	GOD'S SOVEREIGNTY	GOD'S GLORY	
1:1	1:18	3:21	6:1	9:1	12:1	15:

OBSERVATIONS

Key Words and Phrases

11:1 "His people" _____

2 _____

3 _____

4 _____

5 _____

6 _____

7 _____

8 _____

others: _____

Segment Survey

The segment is divided into three paragraphs. Note how Jewish believers are identified in each paragraph: "His people," "remnant," "chosen."

Note the opening question and answer of vers 1. The first paragraph illustrates the answer ou of Old Testament history. What does the secon paragraph do?

_____

_____

About whom is most of the third paragraph?

_____

What one line is about the other people?

_____

Paragraph Analysis

11:1-4
1. How is Paul himself (11:1b) a support of th answer to the question of verse 1a?

_____

_____

2. Read the story of Elijah in 1 Kings 19:9-18 What is the key statement shown in the textua re-creation which is God's testimony about His people? _____

_____

3. What is Paul's statement of God's preservatio of His people? _____

_____

_____

_____

_____

80

11:5-6

1. What is meant by remnant?

_____

_____

How was the remnant of Paul's day related to the remnant of Elijah's time?

_____

_____

2. What determines who are among the remnant? _____

3. What is the key repeated word of verse 6?

_____

4. The word "grace" appears 21 times in Romans. Consult an exhaustive concordance and observe how often the word appears in the New Testament.

11:7-10

1. Do you see grace in this statement about God's people: "those who were chosen obtained it" (11:7)? If so, how?

_____

_____

2. Was God responsible for the unbelievers' hardened hearts (11:7b-10)? Read in the Old Testament the contexts of the verses cited in the margin. This will help you arrive at your answer.

Related Verses

Ps. 94:14 _____

_____

Mark 6:52 _____

_____

Rom. 8:29-30 _____

_____

Rom. 11:25 _____

_____

2 Cor. 3:14-16 _____

_____

Phil. 3:5 _____

_____

James 1:13 _____

INTERPRETATIONS

1. A believing remnant of Jews has existed throughout the nation's history since its beginning with Abraham (Gen. 12). Jews are part of end-time history (e.g., as prophesied in Revelation 7). So the disruption or death of the nation was impossible. "By no means!" (11:1a, NIV). It wasn't hard for Paul to support that answer to the opening question (11:1).

And now, almost 2,000 years later, there is still a believing remnant.

2. "It is by grace" (11:6). What is grace?

_____

_____

Why is grace such a vital part of God's sovereign election? Discuss this with your group.

3. "That which Israel is seeking for" (11:7). These Jews have been seeking for righteousness, but they have been trying to gain it by works. Recall from your study of 10:4-13 (Unit 27) that salvation comes only through faith.

4. "Hardened" (11:7). When a man tries in vain to get God's righteousness by his own works, dullness, blindness, and hardness set in. Then God gives him over to what his heart really wants.

APPLICATIONS

1. This passage reveals much about God and His people. Write a list of these truths, and next to each one record how it can be applied to your life or witness for the Lord.

_____

_____

_____

_____

_____

2. The hardened hearts of unbelievers are very difficult to reach in personal witnessing. What reasons for this are suggested in the descriptions of 11:8-10?

_____

_____

Can you think of ways to bring about softening, with the Lord's help?

_____

_____

Summary of Passage

God has not rejected His people Israel. Down through the ages He has kept for Himself a believing remnant, chosen by Him according to His grace. Elijah was one of them, along with 7,000 other men. And Paul was one of the faithful minority.

The faithless majority, not among the chosen ones, have sought for God's righteousness by works, and have not found it. Instead, their hearts have become more hardened, and dull, and blind.

A Memory Verse   11:5

Looking Ahead

Paul will show how eventually unbelieving Jews will turn and become believers.

SETTING This segment moves on from the preceding paragraph. In 11:7-10 Paul had shown how most Israelites seeking God's righteousness have failed to attain it, and their hearts have become hardened. Now he writes about their future recovery.

SOME JEWS TO BE SAVED

11 I say then,
     they did not STUMBLE **so as to FALL**,
          did they?
                    May it never be!
     But by THEIR TRANSGRESSION
          SALVATION has come
          to the GENTILES,
     to make them **jealous**.
12 Now
     if THEIR TRANSGRESSION
          be **riches** for the WORLD
     and THEIR FAILURE
          be **riches** for the GENTILES,
     how much more
          will THEIR FULFILLMENT BE!

13 But I am speaking
               to you who are GENTILES.
     Inasmuch then
          as I am an apostle of GENTILES,
     I magnify **my ministry**,
14 if **somehow** I might
     (1) move to **jealousy** my fellow-countrymen and
     (2) SAVE some of them,
15 For if
          THEIR REJECTION be
          THE RECONCILIATION of the WORLD,
     what will THEIR ACCEPTANCE be but
                    LIFE from the dead?
16 And if
          the **first piece** of dough be HOLY,
          the lump is **also**;
     and if
          the **root** be HOLY,
          the branches are **too**.

(margin: FAILURE, TO FULFILLMENT)
(margin: REJECTION, TO LIFE)

OBSERVATIONS

Key Words and Phrases

11:11 "fall beyond recovery" (NIV)

11 _____
12 _____
13 _____
14 _____
15 _____
16 _____
others: _____

Segment Survey

First review the preceding paragraph (11:7-10). Then relate the opening question of 11:11 to that. (Note the NIV's extended translation, "so as to fall beyond recovery.") There will be a recovery for Israel, and this passage shows what situation will bring this about.

Book of Romans: GOD'S SALVATION FOR SINNER

P R O L O G U E	NEED OF SALVATION	WAY OF SALVATION	LIFE OF SALVATION	SCOPE OF SALVATION	SERVICES OF SALVATION	E P I L O G U E
		DOCTRINAL			PRACTICAL	
	GOD'S POWER	GOD'S GRACE	GOD'S HOLINESS	GOD'S SOVEREIGNTY	GOD'S GLORY	
1:1	1:18	3:21	6:1	9:1	12:1	15:

Read the two paragraphs. What theme is common to both? _____
_____
_____

Note every reference to Gentiles.
How does Paul identify the Jews?
_____

Mark the textual re-creation to show when the pronouns "they" and "their" refer to the Jews. Why is "jealous(y)" a key word in this segment?
_____
_____
_____
_____

Paragraph Analysis
11:11-12
1. Compare the opening verse (11:11a) with the closing line (11:12b). _____
_____

2. What dark words in the paragraph describe the Jews' spiritual condition before recovery?
_____

What bright words describe the spiritual arena of non-Jews? _____

3. In your own words record how the transformation from FAILURE to FULFILLMENT will take place for Israel. (Compare verse 14 in answering this.) _____
_____
_____

4. What is the significance of Paul's *a fortiori* phrase, "how much more" (11:12)? Note that the NASB translators have inserted an exclamation point at the end of the sentence.
_____
_____

11:13-16
1. What was Paul's strategy in his ministry to the Gentiles (11:13-14)? Why would he make much of ("magnify") that ministry?
_____
_____
_____

_____

2. Relate "save some" (11:14) to "remnant" (11:5).

_____
_____
_____

Related Verses

Num. 15:17-21 _____

_____

Ezek. 37:1-14 _____

_____

Luke 20:16 _____

_____

Acts 9:15; 13:46-49 _____

_____

Rom. 5:11 _____

_____

Rom. 11:25,28 _____

_____

1 Tim. 1:15; 2:4 _____

_____

INTERPRETATIONS

1. "So as to fall" (11:11). As noted above, the intended interpretation is a falling beyond recovery. Paul is writing about Israel **as a nation**. In 11:1-10 he wrote of an unbroken line of remnant. In 11:26 he will disclose that when Jesus returns, Israel will be regathered, judged, and restored to favor.

2. "Salvation has come to the Gentiles" (11:11). The invitation to salvation went out to Gentiles, even to the uttermost parts of the world, after the Jews rejected Christ and His message. (Cf. Rom. 1:17; Acts 9:15; 28:28.)

3. "My fellow-countrymen" (11:14). Here Paul is thinking especially of individual Jews, and his desire is that even "some of them" (11:14) would be saved.

4. "First piece...holy" (11:16). The "first piece" and "root" are Abraham and the patriarchs, who were individual believers. The "lump" and the "branches" are the whole nation Israel, God's chosen people who believe in the Lord. Paul is using the two illustrations to show the **continuity** of the chosen family of Israel, from its birth in Abraham, to its restoration in end-times. (11:26).

APPLICATIONS

1. What do you learn about God's longsuffering and mercy in this passage? How often do you thank Him for this, in your prayers and by your attitudes? _____

_____
_____
_____
_____
_____
_____
_____
_____
_____
_____

2. Once when Paul wrote to the Christians at Corinth he was at a loss for words to describe the grace and salvation which God gives through Christ. So he wrote one exclamatory line to express that: "Thanks be to God for His indescribable gift!" (2 Cor. 9:15). What words of our present unit (Romans 11:11-16) magnify this glorious salvation? How can this spur you on to be a better Christian and witness for Jesus?

_____
_____
_____
_____
_____
_____
_____
_____
_____

Summary of Passage

Israel's sin of rejecting Jesus and His salvation brought about the proclamation of the glad tidings to Gentiles throughout the world. Paul personally made much of his ministry to Gentiles, hoping to move his fellow Jews to jealousy so they would turn to Christ.

Paul knew that Israel had not fallen beyond recovery. Someday their failure will be transformed to fulfillment, and there will be a glorious restoration to life.

A Memory Verse   11:12

Looking Ahead

Paul will speak to believing Gentiles, that they beware of conceit over their present status in God's family.

SETTING In the preceding segment Paul addressed his remarks to Gentile believers in general (cf. 11:13). Now he writes to the Gentiles individually, concerning their relation to Israel.

Book of Romans: GOD'S SALVATION FOR SINNER

P R O L O G U E	NEED OF SALVATION	WAY OF SALVATION	LIFE OF SALVATION	SCOPE OF SALVATION	SERVICES OF SALVATION	E P I L O G U E
		DOCTRINAL			PRACTICAL	
	GOD'S POWER	GOD'S GRACE	GOD'S HOLINESS	GOD'S SOVEREIGNTY	GOD'S GLORY	
1:1	1:18	3:21	6:1	9:1	12:1	15:

INGRAFTED GENTILES

17 But if some of the BRANCHES
                 were **broken off**,
   and you, being a **WILD OLIVE**,
       (1) were **grafted in** among them and
       (2) became **partaker** with them
     of the rich root of the olive tree,
18 do not be ARROGANT
             toward the BRANCHES;
   but if you **are** ARROGANT,
   remember that
      it is **not you** who supports the root,
      but THE ROOT SUPPORTS YOU.

19 You will say then,
     "BRANCHES were **broken off**
       so that I might be **grafted in**."
20 Quite right,
   they were **broken off**
         for their UNBELIEF,
   but you STAND BY YOUR FAITH.
   Do not be **conceited**,
     but FEAR;
21   for if GOD did not **spare**
          the natural BRANCHES,
      neither will HE **spare** YOU.

22 BEHOLD THEN
     the KINDNESS and SEVERITY of GOD;
   to those who **fell**——→ SEVERITY,
   but to you ——→ GOD'S KINDNESS,
   if you **continue** in HIS KINDNESS;
   otherwise
          you **also** will be **cut off.**
23 And they also,
     if they do not **continue** in their UNBELIEF,
         will be **grafted in**;
     for GOD IS ABLE
       to graft them in again.
24 For if you were **cut off**
     from what is by nature a **WILD OLIVE TREE**,
     and were grafted
       contrary to nature
       into a cultivated olive tree,
   HOW MUCH MORE
     shall these who are the **NATURAL BRANCHES**
      be **grafted** into
       their own olive tree?

(side labels: BROKEN BRANCHES: ISRAEL / GRAFTED BRANCHES: GENTILES / VINEDRESSER: GOD)

OBSERVATIONS

Key Words and Phrases

11:17 _____ "branches"
17 _____
17 _____
18 _____
20 _____
20 _____
22 _____
23 _____

others: _____
_____

Segment Survey

Recall from 11:13 that Paul is writing these passages to the Gentiles of the church at Rome. Read the illustration of the olive tree in the first paragraph. Who are the broken-off branches?

_____

Who are grafted branches? _____

What is the command of the paragraph?

_____
_____

What is the command of the second paragraph?

_____
_____

To whom is it directed?

_____

Who is prominent in the third paragraph?

_____
_____

What is the command of this paragraph?

_____
_____

Paragraph Analysis

11:17-18
1. The central phrase of this long sentence is a command to Gentile believers, since they are the ones addressed. Why would Gentiles become arrogant? (Cf. verse 19.)

_____

2. Record three reasons from this paragraph for Gentiles not to be arrogant about Israel:

v. 17b _____

v. 17c _____

v. 18b _____

11:19-21
1. Complete this statement, based on the text:

Jews were broken off God's olive tree

BECAUSE OF _____

IN ORDER THAT _____

Gentiles were grafted in

ON THE BASIS OF _____
NOT BECAUSE of superior worth.

2. How does the warning of 11:21 support the command of 11:20? _____

11:22-24

1. What two attributes of God does Paul make prominent here?_____

2. How does verse 22 expand on the earlier command "Fear" (v. 20b) and verse 21?

3. How do verses 23-24 show Paul's optimism concerning Israel's future?

Related Verses

John 4:22_____

John 15:2_____

Rom. 2:4 _____

1 Cor. 10:12_____

Eph. 2:11 ff. _____

Heb. 3:6,14_____

1 Peter 1:17_____

INTERPRETATIONS

1. "You...were grafted in" (11:17). The metaphor of verse 17 shows wild olive shoots (Gentile Christians) being grafted into the cultivated olive tree (large purposes of God's redeeming grace for sinners), which has healthy branches (Israel) to begin with. So the grafted shoots (Gentiles) draw some nourishment from fatness of the original roots ("the Abrahamic covenant which promised blessing to both Jew and Gentile through Christ"— Ryrie Study Bible, in loc.).

2. "Fear" (11:20). What kind of fear is this, in view of verse 21?_____

3. "Otherwise you also will be cut off" (11:22).

What does Paul say can keep this from happening (11:22)?_____
What do you think that means?
(Cf. John 15:2a,6a.) _____

APPLICATIONS

1. Why is anti-Semitism dangerous and disastrous for the Christian, according to this passage?

How can you help other Gentile Christians to have a good relationship with unsaved Jews? Discuss this with your group.

2. The condition for not being "cut off" from the blessing and goodness of God is for the believer to "continue in God's kindness." Surely this does not mean merely to coast along in our Christian walk. Can you think of Bible passages which exhort the believer to an ever-active life of service and communion with God? Share such Scriptures with your group.

Summary of Passage

Jews who are not of God's remnant have been cut off because of their unbelief. God has grafted Gentile Christians into His olive tree because of their faith. So Gentile believers should not boast or be conceited over the favor shown them. They must fear and respect God's severity and continue to grow in His kindness, lest they also be cut off from His blessing.

One day Israel will be grafted back into the olive tree when they believe, for God is able to do this.

A Memory Verse 11:22
Looking Ahead

Paul will show that when the Gentile age is completed, Israel as a nation will turn to the Lord and be saved.

SETTING Note on the survey chart that this segment concludes the ISRAEL section of Romans. It is the climax of chapters 9–11. Also, note on the chart that Chapter 11 concludes the doctrinal section of Romans.

Book of Romans: GOD'S SALVATION FOR SINNER

P R O L O G U E	NEED OF SALVATION	WAY OF SALVATION	LIFE OF SALVATION	SCOPE OF SALVATION	SERVICES OF SALVATION	
		DOCTRINAL			PRACTICAL	
	GOD'S POWER	GOD'S GRACE	GOD'S HOLINESS	GOD'S SOVEREIGNTY	GOD'S GLORY	
1:1	1:18	3:21	6:1	9:1	12:1	15:

ALL ISRAEL WILL BE SAVED

25 For I do not want you, BRETHREN,
  to be **uninformed** of this MYSTERY,
  lest you be WISE in your own estimation,
  that a PARTIAL HARDENING
    has happened to ISRAEL
  until the FULNESS of the GENTILES
      has come in;
26 and thus
      ALL ISRAEL WILL BE SAVED;
  just as it is written,
    "The DELIVERER will come from ZION,
    He will **remove ungodliness** from Jacob."
              [Isa. 59:20,21]
27 "And this is MY COVENANT with them,
    When I **take away their sins**."   [Isa. 27:9]

EVENT

28 From the standpoint of the GOSPEL
    they are **enemies** for your sake,
  but from the standpoint of GOD'S CHOICE
      they are **beloved** for the sake of the fathers;
29 for
    (1) the **gifts** and
    (2) the **calling** of GOD
        are irrevocable.
30 For just as
    you once were disobedient to GOD
    but now have been shown MERCY
      because of **their disobedience**,
31 so these also
          now have been **disobedient**,
    in order that because of the MERCY
        shown to you
      they also may **now** be shown MERCY
32 For God has shut up all in **disobedience**
    that HE MIGHT SHOW MERCY TO ALL.

MERCY

33 Oh the **depth** of the **riches**
    both of
        (1) the WISDOM and
        (2) KNOWLEDGE of God!
  How
        (1) unsearchable are His JUDGMENTS and
        (2) unfathomable His WAYS!
34 For
      Who has known the MIND of the Lord,
  or Who became His COUNSELOR?   [Isa. 40:13 ff.]
35 or Who has first given to Him
        that it might be paid back to him again?
              [Job 35:7, Job 41:11]
36 For
        (1) from Him and
        (2) through Him and
        (3) to Him
            are ALL THINGS.
  To Him be the GLORY FOREVER.
            Amen.

GLORY

OBSERVATIONS

Key Words and Phrases

11:25   "partial hardening" _____

  25 _____

---

26 _____
26 _____
28 _____
30 _____
33 _____
36 _____
others: _____
_____

Segment Survey

The segment contains three related but differen paragraphs. Read the passage, and record wha is asked for.

11:25-27 What event is prophesied?
_____
_____

11:28-32 What attribute of God is prominent?
_____

11:33-36 How appropriate is this as the conclu sion of the doctrinal section of Romans?
_____
_____

Paragraph Analysis

11:25-27
1. What one word of verse 25 does Paul use t describe the prophecy which he records in th remainder of the paragraph?
_____

2. List the various things that are part of th prophecy of verses 25-27:
_____
_____
_____
_____
_____
_____

11:28-32
1. Identify:
"they" (v. 28) _____
"your" (v. 28) _____
"the fathers" (v. 28) _____
2. What two words are contrasted in verse 28?
_____
3. Record the comparisons of verses 30-31:

86

Gentiles:

once _____

now_____

Jews:

have been _____

now_____

4. Compare the key word of the opening line of the paragraph with the key word of the last line.

_____

11:33-36

1. Observe in the textual re-creation how three groups of lines comprise this paragraph. Record on the chart your own outline of the three parts. Whom is Paul describing here?

_____

2. How does this conclude the three-chapter section on Israel? _____

How does it conclude the doctrinal section of the epistle (chapters 1-11)?

_____
_____
_____

Related Verses

Deut. 10:14-15_____

_____

Luke 21:23-27_____

_____

Acts 15:14-18_____

_____

Rom. 2:4 _____

_____

Rom. 10:12-13_____

_____

Eph. 3:1-7 _____

_____

Heb. 8:10,12_____

_____

INTERPRETATIONS

1. God's rejection of Israel as a nation is not final (11:11). Spiritual blindness in the nation will persist until "the fulness of the Gentiles has come in" (11:25; cf. Mark 13:10 and Luke 21:23-27). This may be interpreted as "until the full number of the Gentiles enters in," (cf. Acts 15:14-18). According to 11:26 Israel's blindness and ungodliness will end with the coming of their Deliverer, Christ, for that is God's covenant with them. Note how the accompanying chart shows us to be living in the church age, and that the second coming of Christ will herald the end of

this Gentile era. (Chart from Irving L. Jensen, *Romans*, Moody Press, p. 89.)

ISRAEL IN RELATION TO THE CHURCH AGE

APPLICATIONS

1. Are you impressed with God's love for *all* sinners, Jew and Gentile? How should this make you a more effective witness to unsaved souls? Also, how should it increase your love to others? (TBS#7)

2. Record some everyday facts that illustrate the sovereignty of God taught in 11:36. Discuss this with your group._____

_____
_____
_____

3. Does this passage, along with the preceding ones, make you more sensitive to how great God is and how small and undeserving you are? Pray now, and open your heart to His efforts to make you a better child and servant.

Summary of Passage

When the full number of Gentiles has come into the family of God, Jesus will return to earth, and all Israel as a nation will turn to Him and be saved.

During this Gentile age, Jews are enemies of the gospel and of the Gentiles, but they are always beloved of God on account of their forefathers, to whom God gave irrevocable promises. They have been and now are disobedient and faithless, but in the end, by the mercy of God which He shows to all, they shall be saved through faith.

How great is God! To Him be the glory forever!

| A Memory Verse | 11:36 |

Looking Ahead

Paul will return to the practical purposes of his letter, urging all-out consecration on the part of all saved people of God.

SERVICE OF SALVATION
12:1–15:13

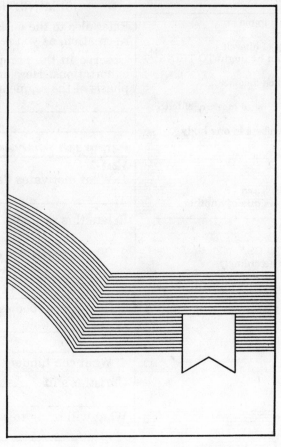

SETTING Note on the survey chart that this segment begins the PRACTICAL section of Romans, which has emphasis on one's every-day conduct, in particular, SERVICE to the glory of God. Duty (chapters 12–15) is based on doctrine (chapters 1–11), so Paul's opening words are "I urge you *therefore*" (12:1).

A LIVING SACRIFICE

1 I **urge you** therefore, BRETHREN,
        by the **MERCIES OF GOD**,
    to PRESENT YOUR BODIES
        (1) a **living** and **holy** SACRIFICE,
        (2) **acceptable** to God, which is
        (3) your **spiritual** SERVICE of WORSHIP.
2 And do not BE CONFORMED to this **world**,
        but BE TRANSFORMED
            by the **renewing of your mind**,
        that you may prove what the **will of God** is,
            that which is good
                and acceptable
                and perfect.

SPIRITUAL SERVICE

3 For through the GRACE given to me
    I say to **every man** among you
    not to THINK **more highly** of himself
                    than he ought TO THINK;
    but to THINK
            so as to have sound judgment,
        as God has allotted to each
                        a measure of faith.
4 For
        just as we have **many** members in **one body**
        and all the members
            do not have the **same** function,
5 so we, who are **many**,
        are
        (1) **one body** IN CHRIST, and
        (2) **individually** members **one of another**.

HUMBLE ESTEEM

6 And since WE HAVE GIFTS
        that **differ** according to
            GRACE GIVEN TO US,
        let each **exercise** them accordingly:
        (1) if PROPHECY,
            according to the proportion of his **faith**;
7   (2) if SERVICE,
            in his serving;
        (3) or he who TEACHES,
            in his teaching;
8   (4) or he who EXHORTS,
            in his exhortation;
        (5) he who GIVES,
            with **liberality**;
        (6) he who LEADS,
            with **diligence**;
        (7) he who SHOWS MERCY,
            with **cheerfulness**.

EXERCISED GIFTS

OBSERVATIONS
Key Words and Phrases

12:1 "present your bodies"
1_____
2_____
3_____
5_____

Book of Romans: GOD'S SALVATION FOR SINNE

P R O L O G U E	NEED OF SALVATION	WAY OF SALVATION	LIFE OF SALVATION	SCOPE OF SALVATION	SERVICES OF SALVATION	
		DOCTRINAL			PRACTICAL	
	GOD'S POWER	GOD'S GRACE	GOD'S HOLINESS	GOD'S SOVEREIGNTY	GOD'S GLORY	
1:1	1:18	3:21	6:1	9:1	12:1	15

6_____
7_____
8_____
others:_____

Segment Survey
The three paragraphs of this segment may b studied as three vital aspects of Christian servic (note the phrase "spiritual service" in 12:1). Kee this outline in mind as you read the paragraphs:

    (1) WORSHIP (12:1-2)
    (2) FELLOWSHIP (12:3-5)
    (3) MINISTRY (12:6-8)

Refer also to the outlines shown on the textua re-creation, as you read the paragraphs.

Observe in the paragraphs the commands an exhortations. How are these a clue to the en phasis of the segment?
_____
_____

Paragraph Analysis
12:1-2
1. What motivates Paul's appeal (12:1)?
_____
Relate this to 11:32._____
2. What are the two commands?
_____
3. How can our *bodies* be used in *spiritual* servi of worship?_____
4. What can hinder the will of God in a Christian's life? _____
What will bring to pass God's will?
_____

12:3-5
1. What one word expresses the command of verse 3?_____
2. How should Christians think of themselves
_____
3. How is this related to the truth of verse 5?
_____

12:6-8

1. What fact about gifts for Christian living does Paul establish in 12:6a?

_____

_____

2. What exhortation follows that?

"let_____ "

3. How many gifts does Paul cite?

_____

Are they only for clergy, or teachers, or laymen? If not, who receives them?

_____

4. For which gifts does Paul add a restrictive appeal?_____

_____

_____

Related Verses

Rom. 6:13_____

_____

1 Cor. 1:7_____

_____

1 Cor. 12:4-31_____

_____

1 Cor. 14:3_____

_____

Eph. 4:7-16_____

_____

1 Tim. 5:17_____

_____

1 Peter 1:13-16_____

_____

1 Peter 4:10-11_____

_____

INTERPRETATIONS

1. The opening paragraph (12:1-2) introduces the entire practical section (12:1–15:7) by appealing for total consecration to the Lord: body, mind and spirit. In your own words, write down what Paul means by the references to these. (Cf. Rom. 3:5-7; Heb. 13:15-16; 1 Peter 2:5.)

_____

_____

_____

2. "Think...as God has allotted to each" (12:3). God allots measures of faith differently to each of His children. The individual portion should determine how each Christian thinks of himself. *The Living Bible* paraphrases: "Be honest in your estimate of yourselves, measuring your value by

how much faith God has given you" (12:3b).

3. The "gifts" of 12:6-8 are abilities God gives believers so they may serve Him effectively as part of the body of Christ. God gives some servants many gifts; all are given at least one (cf. 1 Peter 4:10). The gift of prophecy is one of inspired utterance of God's truth, such as preaching (cf. 1 Cor. 14:3).

Discuss with your group the three New Testament lists of spiritual gifts, given in these passages: Romans 12:6-8; 1 Corinthians 12:28; Ephesians 4:11.

APPLICATIONS

1. Our physical bodies, our thought-life and the world around us are three of the most difficult testing-grounds for our Christian faith. So it does not surprise us that Paul focuses on these in his introductory appeal of the practical part of his letter. Discuss with your group these and related subjects:

(a) areas of temptation regarding the physical body (sex is only *one* of these)
(b) how our thought-life controls our day
(c) the allurements of the world to all people, including Christians.

In your discussions of the "enemies," share testimonies with each other how God has helped you with victory, according to His promises (e.g. 7:24-25).

2. God gives grace and faith to all His children (12:3,6). He gives the spiritual gifts not for the having but for the exercising. What gift has He given you? How faithfully and effectively are you using it? What are your motivations? Is God being glorified? Is there any fruit (seen or unseen)? Spend much time reflecting on this subject, because your service for God stems from what He gives you.

Summary of Passage

All Christians should offer themselves totally—body, soul and spirit—to God and His service. They should not conform to the world's pattern, but be new and different persons in thought, word and deed. They should be humble about their place in the fellowship of believers, which is the body of Christ, and they should honor and serve their brethren. In their service for God they should exercise to the fullest, by faith, the spiritual gift He has given them, according to the measure He has allotted.

A Memory Verse   12:1

Looking Ahead

Paul writes about the Christian's obligations to other people, whether believers or unbelievers.

SETTING Paul has just written about spiritual gifts which God gives His children for service. Now he applies this to real situations, as he writes about the Christian servant's obligations to others.

Book of Romans: GOD'S SALVATION FOR SINNE

P R O L O G U E	NEED OF SALVATION	WAY OF SALVATION	LIFE OF SALVATION	SCOPE OF SALVATION	SERVICES OF SALVATION	
			DOCTRINAL		PRACTICAL	
	GOD'S POWER	GOD'S GRACE	GOD'S HOLINESS	GOD'S SOVEREIGNTY	GOD'S GLORY	
1:1	1:18	3:21	6:1	9:1	12:1	15:

others: _____

DO WHAT IS RIGHT

9 Let LOVE be without **hypocrisy**.
   Abhor what is EVIL;
   cling to what is GOOD.
10 Be devoted to one another
                              in BROTHERLY LOVE;
   give preference to one another
                              in HONOR;
11 not lagging behind in DILIGENCE,
      fervent in SPIRIT,
         SERVING the LORD;
12 **rejoicing** in HOPE,
   persevering in TRIBULATION,
   devoted to PRAYER,
13   **contributing to** the NEEDS of the SAINTS,
         practicing HOSPITALITY.

FELLOW-CHRISTIANS

14 BLESS those who persecute you;
   ——▶ BLESS and curse not.
15 REJOICE with those who **rejoice**, and
   WEEP with those who **weep**.
16 Be of the **same mind** toward one another;
   do **not** be **haughty** in mind,
      but ASSOCIATE with the **lowly**.
   Do **not** be **wise** in **your own estimation**.
17 Never pay back **evil for evil** to anyone.
   RESPECT what is RIGHT
               in the sight of ALL MEN.
18 If possible,
      so far as it depends on **you**,
         be at peace with all men.

ALL MEN

19 Never take your own **revenge**, BELOVED,
   but ——▶ leave room for the WRATH OF GOD,
            for it is written,
      "VENGEANCE IS MINE,
      I will repay, says the Lord."
                              [Prov. 20:22, 24:29]
20 "But if your **enemy** is **hungry**,
               FEED HIM,
   and if he is **thirsty**,
               GIVE HIM A DRINK;
                              [Prov. 25:21 ff.]
   for in so doing
      you will heap **burning coals** upon his **head**."
21 Do not be OVERCOME BY EVIL,
   but OVERCOME EVIL WITH GOOD.

ENEMY

OBSERVATIONS

Key Words and Phrases

12:9 "love" _____
   11 _____
   12 _____
   13 _____
   15 _____
   18 _____
   19 _____
   21 _____

Segment Survey

As you read the segment for the first time, coun how many commands and exhortations there are This will help you to see how practical the epistl is in these latter chapters.

The segment shows the obligations which th Christian servant has to all people—saved an unsaved. In the first paragraph the specific iden tifications of people in need are our fellow-Chris tians. Mark the references in the textual re-cre ation. All men are the objects in the second para graph. Who are seen in the last paragraph?

_____

Where in the text does the title DO WHAT I RIGHT come from? _____

Paragraph Analysis

12:9-13
1. Compare the opening verse of the paragrap (v. 9) with the closing verse of the segment (v 21). Observe among other things both the nega tive and positive commands.

_____

Recall from an earlier study that the New Testa ment word "godliness" (e.g. 1 Tim. 2:2) mean literally "revering that which is good."
2. What is the first command of the segment?

_____

How is love the foundation to all the Christian obligations to others? _____

3. How does love appear in other commands c the paragraph? _____

_____

4. In what ways do the six attitudes referred t in verses 11-12 help your ministry to other Christians? _____

_____

12:14-18
Paul wants his readers always to be in open cor tact with all people, identifying with their need and associating with them on their level. Wha does each verse say about this?

_____
_____
_____
_____
_____

12:19-21
What is the main point of the paragraph?

_____
_____

Related Verses

2 Kings 6:22 _____

Matt. 5:43-45 _____

John 13:34 _____
_____

Rom. 14:19 _____
_____

1 Cor. 4:12 _____

2 Cor. 6:6 _____

1 Thess. 5:15 _____
_____

Heb. 10:32-35 _____
_____

Heb. 13:3 _____

INTERPRETATIONS

1. "Love...without hypocrisy" (12:9). Record some examples of hypocritical love among Christians.
_____
_____

2. "Fervent in spirit" (12:11). This is the spiritual fervor of the Christian servant. Although the word "spirit" here does not refer to the third Person of the Trinity, the Holy Spirit is the source of the believer's fervor.

3. What does it mean to "bless those who persecute you" (12:14)? _____
_____
_____

4. "Associate with the lowly" (12:16). Recall some of Jesus' words and activities that illustrate this.
_____
_____
_____

5. "Respect what is right" (12:17). In your own words, what is right?

_____
_____
_____

6. "If possible...be at peace" (12:18). When might it not be possible to be at peace with others?

_____
_____

7. Justify the motivation of 11:20b, in feeding a hungry enemy. _____
_____
_____

APPLICATIONS

1. Apply the first paragraph to your own life. How do you measure according to these standards concerning your relationships with other Christians? Record those areas where you need to improve, and pray continually to God for victory in these.

_____
_____
_____
_____

2. Read the second and third paragraphs again. As you do, note the things that will help you be a better witness for Jesus to unsaved souls. Record these, and share them with members of your group.

_____
_____
_____
_____
_____

Summary of Passage

All Christians should be devoted to one another in brotherly love, seeking ways to help them in their daily needs.

Believers should also maintain close and warm relationships with all believers—even with those who oppose their Christian stand. As much as possible, believers should live at peace with everyone, and leave all vengeance to God, who knows all, and who will repay justly.

A Memory Verse   12:20

Looking Ahead

Paul writes about the Christian's obligations to earthly rulers and authorities.

SETTING Chapter 13 discusses the Christian citizen, pointing out that Christians are not in isolation but are members of churches, organizations, and countries. So the Spirit moved Paul in this segment to include practical exhortations about Christian subjection to authorities over them.

SUBMIT TO AUTHORITIES

1 Let every person
  be in SUBJECTION
    to the governing AUTHORITIES.
 For there is no AUTHORITY
    except FROM GOD,
 and those which exist
    are ESTABLISHED by GOD.
2 Therefore
  he who **resists** AUTHORITY
 has opposed the **ORDINANCE** of GOD;
 and they who have opposed
  will receive CONDEMNATION upon themselves.

AUTHORITIES FROM GOD

3 For RULERS are
  not a cause of FEAR for **good behavior,**
  but for **evil.**
  Do you want to have **no fear** of AUTHORITY?
 Do what is **good,**
  and you will have PRAISE from the same;
4 for it is
    a MINISTER OF GOD to you for **good.**
 But if you do what is **evil,**
  be afraid;
 for it does not bear the **sword** for nothing;
  for it is a MINISTER OF GOD,
    an **avenger**
 who brings **wrath** upon the one
     who practices **evil.**

AUTHORITIES FOR GOOD

5 Wherefore
 it is necessary to be in SUBJECTION,
  not only because of **wrath,**
  but also for **conscience'** sake.
6 For because of this
    you also PAY TAXES,
 for RULERS are SERVANTS of GOD,
    devoting themselves to this very thing.
7 Render to ALL what is DUE them:
  (1) tax to whom tax is due;
  (2) custom to whom custom;
  (3) fear to whom fear;
  (4) honor to whom honor.

SUPPORT THE AUTHORITIES

OBSERVATIONS

Key Words and Phrases

13:1 "governing authorities _____

 2 _____

 2 _____

 3 _____

 4 _____

 5 _____

 6 _____

 7 _____

others: _____

Book of Romans: GOD'S SALVATION FOR SINNERS

P R O L O G U E	NEED OF SALVATION	WAY OF SALVATION	LIFE OF SALVATION	SCOPE OF SALVATION	SERVICES OF SALVATION	E P I L O G U E
		DOCTRINAL			PRACTICAL	
	GOD'S POWER	GOD'S GRACE	GOD'S HOLINESS	GOD'S SOVEREIGNTY	GOD'S GLORY	
1:1	1:18	3:21	6:1	9:1	12:1	15:1

Segment Survey

1. Read the segment, observing the ways authorities are identified. Record these:

_____

_____

_____

2. Note the outline shown with the textual recreation, identifying a different emphasis in each paragraph. Read the paragraphs again and justify this outline.

3. Does Paul write this passage just to Christians? Support your answer by the text.

_____

_____

Paragraph Analysis

13:1-2

1. What is the origin of governing authorities in the world?_____

2. For whom?_____

3. What is the price of opposition?_____

_____

13:3-4

1. What two kinds of fear does Paul mention?

_____

_____

2. Record the different contrasts of this paragraph._____

_____

_____

_____

3. Where in the paragraph does this combination appear?

MINISTER OF GOD ⬧ MINISTER FOR GOOD

_____

Recall your study of the word "good" in the practical section of the epistle.

4. Where in the paragraph does this combination appear:

 MINISTER OF GOD ⬧ AVENGER WITH WRATH

Compare this with the last line of the first paragraph.

_____

_____

_____

_____

13:5-7

1. What reasons does Paul give for obeying the authorities? _____
_____
_____
_____

2. What do subjects owe their rulers and law officers? _____
_____
_____

Related Verses

Jer. 27:5 ff. _____
_____

Ecc. 8 _____
_____

Matt. 17:24 ff. _____
_____

Matt. 22:21 _____
_____

John 19:11 _____
_____

1 Tim. 2:1-4 _____
_____

Titus 3:1 _____
_____

1 Peter 2:13-19 _____
_____

INTERPRETATIONS

1. "There is no authority except from God" (13:1; cf. Dan. 2:21,37). God established the principle of government and authority, even though some governments do not meet His specifications. When Paul wrote Romans, the tyrant Nero was the Roman Empire's ruler. (Read Deuteronomy 17:14-20 to see God's interest in Israel's government.)

2. "Resists authority" (13:2). Citizens are commanded not to resist authority, though they may and should protest evil and ungodliness in the organization.

3. "For conscience' sake" (13:5). The Christian knows he must submit to the authorities. If he doesn't do this, he will reap punishment and incur a guilty conscience.

4. "Pay taxes" (13:6). One of Paul's reasons for this command is that the authorities "give their full time to governing" (13:6b, NIV), that is, this is their livelihood.

5. Interpret 13:7 in light of Mark 12:17, and record your observations. Also discuss this with your group.

_____
_____
_____
_____

APPLICATIONS

1. God is the author of law and order. His creation reflects this. Without order there would be chaos, not cosmos. The universe is one ("uni") because God in Christ holds everything together (Col. 1:17).

What can you learn from this, and apply in such practical things as stewardship of time, energy and money, and in orderliness in performing your Christian ministries? (Discuss this with your group, suggesting other ways also.)

2. How can you influence young people to respect civil authority ("honor to whom honor"—13:7)?

_____
_____
_____
_____

3. Mark 12:17 is usually referred to for its command about rendering to Caesar. Its other command is "Render to God the things that are God's." What things are God's? How does this touch your life? Discuss this important subject with your group.

Summary of Passage

God commands everyone to submit to the governing authorities, because He has established the authorities in the world for good. Those who do not submit to the civil rulers will reap punishment and a guilty conscience. Those who do submit and pay all that is due, including respect and taxes, will live free from the fear of recompense.

A Memory Verse   13:1

Looking Ahead

Paul exhorts Christians to walk in love and light during these days.

SETTING This segment completes Paul's essay on the Christian Citizen (chapter 13). Recall that the first essay (chapter 12) was about the Christian Servant. The third message (14:1–15:7) concerns the Christian Brother.

Book of Romans: GOD'S SALVATION FOR SINNER

P R O L O G U E	NEED OF SALVATION	WAY OF SALVATION	LIFE OF SALVATION	SCOPE OF SALVATION	SERVICES OF SALVATION	E P I L O G U E
		DOCTRINAL			PRACTICAL	
	GOD'S POWER	GOD'S GRACE	GOD'S HOLINESS	GOD'S SOVEREIGNTY	GOD'S GLORY	
1:1	1:18	3:21	6:1	9:1	12:1	15:

LOVE ONE ANOTHER

8　Owe nothing to anyone
　　　except ——→ to LOVE ONE ANOTHER;
　　for he who **LOVES** his neighbor
　　　　　　　　has FULFILLED the **LAW**.
9 For this,
　　　"You shall not **commit adultery**
　　　You shall not **murder**,　　[Ex. 20:13 ff.]
　　　You shall not **steal**,　　[Deut. 5:17 ff.]
　　　You shall not **covet**."
　　and if there is **any other commandment**,
　　　　　　it is summed up in this saying,
　　"You shall LOVE YOUR NEIGHBOR
　　　　　　AS YOURSELF."　　[Lev. 19:18]
10　　LOVE does no wrong to a neighbor;
　　LOVE therefore is
　　　　　　the FULFILLMENT of the **LAW**.

LOVE

11 And this DO,
　　knowing THE TIME,
　　● that it is **already** the hour
　　　　　　for you to **awaken** from sleep;
　　● for now SALVATION is **nearer to us**
　　　　　　than when we **believed**.
12 ● The NIGHT is **almost** gone, and
　　● the DAY is at **hand**.
　　　　　　Let us therefore
　　(1) lay aside the **deeds of darkness** and
　　(2) PUT ON the **armor of light**.
13 (3) Let us behave **properly**
　　　　　　as in the DAY,
　　　(a) not in carousing and drunkenness,
　　　(b) not in sexual promiscuity and sensuality,
　　　(c) not in strife and jealousy.
14 But PUT ON the LORD JESUS CHRIST,
　　and make no provision for the **flesh**
　　　　　　in regard to its **lusts**.

LIGHT

OBSERVATIONS

Key Words and Phrases

13:8 "love one another" _____

8 _____

9 _____

9 _____

11 _____

11 _____

12 _____

13 _____

others: _____

_____

Segment Survey

1. What is the key subject of the first paragraph? _____

_____

2. How does the opening phrase of the second paragraph relate the two paragraphs?

_____

_____

3. What word appropriately identifies the second paragraph? What is its connection with the setting of the paragraph?

_____

_____

4. Compare the word "love" of the opening verse with the last word of the segment.

_____

_____

5. What specific references to Persons of the Trinity appear in the segment?

_____

Paragraph Analysis

13:8-10

1. What do the three emphatic words, "nothing," "anyone," and "except" add to the importance of the command to love one another?

_____

_____

2. How does Paul show love of neighbor to be the fulfillment of the law of God?

_____

_____

_____

13:11-14

1. Read the paragraph again and in your own words briefly complete the thought of the first two lines:

" _____, knowing that the tim

_____

2. What is at hand (13:11,12)?

_____

3. What are the three exhortations of verses 12-13? _____

_____

4. What is the command of verse 14?

_____

_____

Relate this to the second appeal of verse 12. (Cf. Ephesians 6:13 ff.) _____

5. Record the negatives and positives in each of verses 12-14:

Verse	NEGATIVE	POSITIVE
12		
13		
14		

6. What three areas of sin are identified in verse 13? Is there any hint as to difference or degree? How is this significant?

_____

_____

Related Verses

Luke 10:25-37 _____

_____

Luke 21:34-36 _____

_____

Gal. 3:27 _____

_____

Eph. 6:13 ff. _____

_____

1 Thess. 5:8 _____

_____

James 5:7-11 _____

_____

1 Peter 4:7-11 _____

_____

INTERPRETATIONS

1. "He who loves his neighbor has fulfilled the law" (13:8). Read the Ten Commandments in Exodus 20:1-26. In what sense are all the commandments (e.g. the first one) "summed up in this saying, 'You shall love your neighbor as yourself'" (13:9)?

_____

_____

2. "Salvation is nearer to us than when we believed" (13:11). As noted in an earlier unit, salvation has three aspects: we *were* saved at the time of regeneration; we are being saved—our present sanctification; and we shall be saved—including the redemption of our bodies at the moment of transformation into Christ's image. This future experience, the culmination of our salvation, will take place when Christ returns. So "salvation is nearer to us than when we believed."

3. "Armor of light" (13:12). What does this metaphor suggest about the Christian's exposure to Satan's temptations?

_____

4. "Put on the Lord Jesus Christ" (13:14). What does this metaphor suggest about the Christian's being clothed with Jesus Christ?

_____

_____

APPLICATIONS

1. One of your biggest daily tests lies in your relationship to other people. Do you love each one as you love yourself? Is the love for everyone genuine, or is it hypocritical for some, or partial, or even conditional? Write down names of people for whom you do not have the full and genuine love that Paul writes about. Examine your heart for reasons of the shortcomings. And seek the Lord's help in this, to "owe *nothing* to *anyone except* to LOVE" him (13:8).

2. Another big daily test for you may stem from a desire to "gratify the desires of your sinful nature" (13:14, NIV). Recall your earlier study of the struggle going on in your heart because of the two natures, old and new (7:15-25). Compare 7:25a with 13:14a. Keep in close touch with Jesus, who is *THE* answer to those struggles. And also remember the other important commands in this passage about temptations:

(1) "lay aside the deeds of darkness" (13:12)
(2) "make no provision for the flesh in regard to its lusts" (13:14)

Summary of Passage

Love of one's neighbor is the fulfillment of the law of God. So we are to owe nothing to anyone except to love one another. This is especially needy because these are dark and trying days, and our salvation is nearer than ever before.

Temptations to sin are many, and for victory we need to lay aside the deeds of darkness and make no provision for gratifying the desires of our sinful nature. For these battles we have been given armor of light, and for acceptance by the Father we are to clothe ourselves with the Lord Jesus Christ.

Memory Verses   13:11,12

Looking Ahead

Paul begins his essay on the Christian Brother, writing here about the principle of liberty.

SETTING The section on *the Christian Brother* (14:1–15:13) discusses the Christian's position when there are differing opinions over non-essentials. The passage of this unit is the first of three parts, as shown below:

(1) principle of liberty—
key: tolerance   (14:1-12)

(2) principle of love—
key: care   (14:13-23)

(3) example of Christ—
key: obedience   (15:1-13)

WHO ARE YOU TO JUDGE?

1   Now ACCEPT the one
           who is **weak** in the faith,
but not for the purpose
      of passing **judgment** on his opinions.
2   One man has faith that he may eat all things,
but he who is **weak** eats vegetables only.
3 Let not **him who eats** regard with CONTEMPT
        him who does not eat,
and let not **him who does not eat** JUDGE
        him who eats,
for GOD HAS ACCEPTED HIM. ◄
4 Who are you to JUDGE
                the servant of **another**?
To his own master
         he STANDS or FALLS;
and **STAND** he will,
for the LORD IS ABLE
        to MAKE HIM STAND. ◄

COMMAND

5 **One man** regards one day above another,
another regards every day **alike**.
       Let each man be **fully convinced**
           in his own mind.
6 (1) He who observes the day,
         observes it FOR THE LORD, and
     (2) he who eats,
        does so FOR THE LORD,
           for he **gives thanks to God**; and
     (3) he who eats not,
        FOR THE LORD he does not eat,
        and gives thanks to God.
7 For **not one of us**   lives FOR HIMSELF,
    and **not one**   dies FOR HIMSELF;
8 for if we live,
          we live FOR THE LORD,
   or if we die,
          we die FOR THE LORD;
therefore
          whether we live or die,
         WE ARE THE LORD'S. ◄
9 For to this end
       CHRIST died and lived again,
     that He might be LORD
       both of the DEAD
       and of the LIVING.

REASONS

10 But you, ──► why do you JUDGE your brother?
Or you again,
──► why do you REGARD your brother
                with CONTEMPT?
For **we shall all stand**
      BEFORE the JUDGMENT-SEAT of GOD.
11 For it is written,
"As I live, says the Lord,
  (1) every knee shall BOW TO ME, and
  (2) every tongue shall

JUDGMENT-SEAT OF GOD

Book of Romans: GOD'S SALVATION FOR SINNER

P R O L O G U E	NEED OF SALVATION	WAY OF SALVATION	LIFE OF SALVATION	SCOPE OF SALVATION	SERVICES OF SALVATION	E P I L O G U E
		DOCTRINAL			PRACTICAL	
	GOD'S POWER	GOD'S GRACE	GOD'S HOLINESS	GOD'S SOVEREIGNTY	GOD'S GLORY	
1:1	1:18	3:21	6:1	9:1	12:1	15:1

GIVE PRAISE TO GOD."   [Isa. 45:23]
12 So then, **each one of us**
    shall GIVE ACCOUNT OF HIMSELF TO GOD.

OBSERVATIONS

Key Words and Phrases

14:1 "weak in the faith" _____

1 _____

3 _____

5 _____

6 _____

8 _____

10 _____

11 _____

others: _____

_____

Segment Survey

First, read the entire segment and mark on the textual re-creation where any commands appear. Are there many or few commands? Mostly, what does Paul do in the passage?

_____

_____

Study the outline shown on the textual re-creation. Then read each paragraph again and observe how the text is represented by the outline points, in a general way.

Note how each paragraph closes. Who is the key person mentioned, and what point is made?

_____

_____

Paragraph Analysis

14:1-4
1. What is the opening command?

_____

How is this expanded in the latter half of verse 1?

_____

2. What three objects of judging does Paul mention?

(1) _____ "the one who is weak in the faith" (14:1)

(2) _____

(3) _____

May the weak person be guilty of judging another person?
3. Who has the right to judge a servant?

_____

4. How is God brought into this example of legitimate judging? _____

4:5-9

1. How do verses 5 and 6 teach the principles of liberty and diversity? _____

2. What are the common qualifiers in each example of liberty, according to verses 5b and 6?

_____

How does Paul expand on this in verses 7-9, by this truth: "whether we live or die, we are the Lord's"? _____

14:10-12

1. What is Paul's powerful answer to the question, "Why do you judge..."?

2. Note the words "all," "every," and "each one." What do they contribute to this discussion about judging one another?

3. Relate verse 12 to verse 5b. _____

Related Verses

Matt. 12:36 _____

_____

Rom. 15:1 _____

_____

1 Cor. 3:10-15 _____

_____

1 Cor. 10:25-31 _____

_____

2 Cor. 5:10 _____

_____

Col. 2:16-23 _____

_____

1 Tim. 4:3-5 _____

_____

James 4:12 _____

_____

INTERPRETATIONS

1. "But not for...passing judgment" (14:1). Welcoming a Christian brother into your fellowship is not genuine if you take advantage of his being weaker in the faith than you, by judging his opinions.

2. There are some areas of conduct which may be amoral (neither right nor wrong). In *all* things, including these, God is the judge (14:11-12). God accepts (14:3) both the vegetarian and the non-vegetarian, provided their heart and motives are right. What are such qualifiers which Paul cites in this passage:

v. 5b _____

v. 6a _____

v. 6b _____

3. Use the *Living Bible* paraphrase for your study of 14:9b: "so that he can be our Lord while we live and when we die."

4. "The judgment seat of God" (14:10). This is not the great white throne judgment (Revelation 20:11 ff.), when unbelievers will be judged. Compare the wording of Romans 14:11 with Philippians 2:10-11.

A judgment for believers only will take place after the church is raptured. This is the judgment seat (*bema*) of Christ, which Paul writes about in 1 Corinthians 3:10-15 and 2 Corinthians 5:10. It will not be a judgment for sins but an examination of works, the outcome of which will bring rewards or loss of rewards.

APPLICATIONS

1. God grieves over division and conflict in churches and other Christian groups. Yet Christians have the strongest reasons for unity and love, because they comprise the one body of Christ. The passage of this lesson establishes some ruling principles of attitude and action over debatable areas of conduct or differing opinions on non-essentials. In Paul's day, food and holidays were such non-essentials. Near the end of the epistle (16:17) he will refer to a major area of *essentials* in the church, that of sound Christian doctrine.

What questions about non-essentials or personal preferences can threaten unity in Christian fellowships today? How can you help the cause of unity? Discuss this with your group.

2. Another example of cliques in the Christian group appears in this passage, indirectly. In every Christian group there are different levels of maturity in the Christian faith, from weak to strong, and from the little-instructed to the much-instructed. How can all Christians in a group help to keep unity in such diversity? Discuss this also with your group.

Summary of Passage

All Christians should accept one another in their fellowship, even though there may be differing opinions and conduct over things not clearly identified in Scripture. Each believer has the liberty to take his own position, and he should do this in an attitude of (1) thanks to God, (2) a desire to honor Him as Lord, and (3) acknowledgement that he must one day give an account of himself to the Lord.

Memory Verses   14:7,8

Looking Ahead

Paul urges his readers to love one another and not put stumbling blocks in their way.

SETTING In the preceding passage Paul showed how the principle of liberty should motivate Christians of differing opinions to avoid judging one another. Now he appeals to the principle of love to activate believers in building up each other, rather than putting obstacles in each other's pathway.

BUILD UP ONE ANOTHER

13 Therefore
   let us not **judge one another** anymore,
   but rather **determine** this—
   not to put an **obstacle**
         or a **stumbling block** in a brother's way.
14 I know and
   am convinced in the LORD JESUS
        that nothing is UNCLEAN in itself;
   but to him who **THINKS** anything to be UNCLEAN,
   to him IT IS UNCLEAN.
15 For if because of **food** your brother is **HURT**,
   you are no longer **WALKING** according to LOVE.
      DO NOT DESTROY with your **food**
        HIM for whom CHRIST DIED.
16 Therefore do not let what is for **you** a good thing
   be spoken of as **evil**;
17 for the KINGDOM OF GOD
   is not eating and drinking
   but
      (1) righteousness and
      (2) peace and
      (3) joy in the HOLY SPIRIT.
18 For he who in **this** way SERVES CHRIST
   is
      (1) acceptable to GOD and
      (2) approved by men.

19 So then **let us pursue** the things
   which make for
      (1) **peace** and
      (2) the **building up** of one another.
20 Do **not tear down** the WORK OF GOD
        for the sake of **food**.
   All things indeed are **clean**,
   but they are **evil**
      for the man who eats and gives offense.
21 It is good not to eat meat or to drink wine,
   or to do anything by which your brother **stumbles**.

22 The FAITH which YOU HAVE,
      Have as **your own conviction** before GOD.
   Happy is he who does not condemn himself
        in what he approves.
23 But he who **doubts**
   is condemned if he eats,
      because his eating is NOT FROM FAITH;
   and whatever is NOT FROM FAITH
      is SIN.

(margin labels, top to bottom: DO NOT DESTROY / PURSUE PEACE / BE CONSISTENT)

OBSERVATIONS
Key Words and Phrases

14:13 "stumbling block" _____

  14 _____

  15 _____

  15 _____

  17 _____

  19 _____

Book of Romans: GOD'S SALVATION FOR SINNE

P R O L O G U E	NEED OF SALVATION	WAY OF SALVATION	LIFE OF SALVATION	SCOPE OF SALVATION	SERVICES OF SALVATION
		DOCTRINAL			PRACTICAL
	GOD'S POWER	GOD'S GRACE	GOD'S HOLINESS	GOD'S SOVEREIGNTY	GOD'S GLORY
1:1	1:18	3:21	6:1	9:1	12:1	1!

  20 _____

  23 _____

others: _____

Segment Survey

As you read the segment for the first time, ob serve the commands and exhortations. Mar these in the textual re-creation. Note also th different references to the Persons of the Trinity

What two people does this passage identify?

_____

_____

Does the passage intend help for the weake brother only, or for the strong also? If the latte what kinds of help does he get?

_____

_____

_____

_____

Paragraph Analysis
14:13-18
1. First read Mark 7:14-23, noting how Jesu declared all foods clean. In the ceremonial law of the Old Testament certain foods were declared unclean (Lev. 11). Some young, weak believer were slow to understand and appropriate deliver ance from the Old Testament legalism, brough about by Christ's new covenant. what does Pau concede to the weak brother in 14b?

_____

In light of that, what must the stronger believe do, when in contact with a weaker brother

(14:15,16)? _____

2. How does verse 17 relate to both the weak an

the strong Christian? _____

3. How does verse 18 expand on that?

_____

_____

_____

14:19-21
1. What two positive things does Paul exhort?

_____

2. Compare the command of verse 20 with the command of verse 15. What do you learn from this?_____

_____

_____

_____

14:22-23
Who is referred to in verse 22?

_____

In verse 23?_____ .
Paraphrase each verse in your own words. Then compare the reading of the *Living Bible*.

Related Verses

Mark 7:14-23_____

Acts 10:15_____

1 Cor. 8:7-13_____

1 Cor. 10:23,29-33_____

Gal. 5:22,23_____

Eph. 5:2_____

2 Tim. 2:22,23 _____

INTERPRETATIONS
1. "Stumbling block" (14:13). In the context, a stumbling block refers to a temptation to sin.
2. "Because of food" (14:15). Read this as "because of what you eat" (NIV).
3. "The kingdom of God" (14:17). In effect Paul is saying "Why ruin a wonderful thing—Kingdom living, or Christian living—by such a small irritation—over eating and drinking?" Then how does Paul describe Christian living (14:17b,18)?_____

_____

4. Read verse 22 this way: "So whatever you believe about these things keep between yourself and God." (NIV) Faith here means a conviction about something, or a standard. *The Living Bible* paraphrases the last of 14:23 this way: "Anything that is done apart from what he feels is right is sin."

APPLICATIONS
1. Write two lists from this passage about the problem: things not to do, and things to do.

THINGS NOT TO DO	THINGS TO DO

Can you think of activities, not evil of themselves, which you should forego in the presence of a weaker Christian? How difficult is this to do? Explain._____

_____

_____

_____

_____

2. What encouragement and motivation do you get by knowing how the three Persons of the Trinity are intimately involved in solving practical problems like these?

_____

_____

_____

_____

Summary of Passage
A Christian must not put a stumbling block in a weaker brother's way by participating in something which the brother thinks is sin. By doing that unloving act, he will destroy him, wipe out peace and joy, and tear down the work which God had done up to that time.

Christians should be trying always to build up one another in love.

A Memory Verse   14:19
Looking Ahead
Paul shows how Christ is a good example of one who unselfishly acted in behalf of others in their needs.

SETTING Paul concludes his discussion of *the Christian Brother* by reminding his readers of the example of Christ. Our Lord's example is the best instruction that can be given for dealing with problems of division such as Chapter 14 cites.

Note on the survey chart that this passage concludes the main body of the epistle (DOCTRINAL—PRACTICAL, 1:18–15:13) before the EPILOGUE begins.

PLEASE YOUR NEIGHBOR

1 Now we who are STRONG
  ought to bear the weaknesses
                of those **without strength**
  and **not** just please ourselves.
2 Let each of us please his neighbor
    (1) for his GOOD,
    (2) to his EDIFICATION.
3 For even CHRIST did **not** please Himself;
    but as it is written,
    "The **reproaches** of those who **reproached** Thee
      fell upon Me."   [Ps. 69:9]
4 For whatever was written in earlier times
              was written FOR OUR INSTRUCTION,
    that
        (1) through PERSEVERANCE and
        (2) the ENCOURAGEMENT
            of the SCRIPTURES
                        we might have HOPE.

5 Now may the GOD who gives
        (1) PERSEVERANCE and
        (2) ENCOURAGEMENT
    grant you to be of the **same mind**
                with one another
                according to CHRIST JESUS;
6 that **with one accord**
  you may **with one voice**
              GLORIFY the GOD
              and FATHER of our LORD JESUS CHRIST.

7 **Wherefore,** ACCEPT one another,
      just as CHRIST also ACCEPTED us
    to the **GLORY OF GOD.**
8 For I say that CHRIST has become a SERVANT
      to the circumcision
        on behalf of the **TRUTH OF GOD**
          (1) to confirm the **promises**
              given to the **fathers,** and
9   (2) for the GENTILES
            to GLORIFY GOD for **HIS MERCY;**
    as it is written, "Therefore I will give **PRAISE** to Thee
                    among the GENTILES,
    And I will **SING** to Thy name."   [Ps. 18:49]
10 And again he says,
    "**Rejoice,** O GENTILES, with His people."
                                        [Deut. 32:43]
11 And again, "Praise the LORD all you GENTILES,
    And let **all the peoples** praise HIM."   [Ps. 117:1]
12 And again Isaiah says,
    "There shall come the **root** of Jesse,
    And He who ARISES TO RULE over the GENTILES;
    In HIM shall the GENTILES HOPE."   [Isa. 11:10]

13 Now may the GOD OF HOPE fill you
      with all JOY and PEACE in **believing,**
        that you may abound in HOPE
            by the POWER of the HOLY SPIRIT.

PLEASE YOUR NEIGHBOR — *-benediction-* — *ACCEPT ONE ANOTHER* — *-benediction-*

Book of Romans: GOD'S SALVATION FOR SINNER

P R O L O G U E	NEED OF SALVATION	WAY OF SALVATION	LIFE OF SALVATION	SCOPE OF SALVATION	SERVICES OF SALVATION	
		DOCTRINAL			PRACTICAL	
	GOD'S POWER	GOD'S GRACE	GOD'S HOLINESS	GOD'S SOVEREIGNTY	GOD'S GLORY	
1:1	1:18	3:21	6:1	9:1	12:1	15

OBSERVATIONS

Key Words and Phrases

15:1 "we who are strong" _____

2 _____

3 _____

5 _____

6 _____

7 _____

8 _____

9 _____

others: _____

Segment Survey

Note the layout of the four paragraphs on th textual re-creation chart. View each benedictio as the outcome of each preceding paragraph. A you read the four paragraphs, keep in mind tha this is Paul's conclusion to the main body of th epistle. How does this explain its high, positiv note? _____

What are the two commands of the first and thir paragraphs? _____

How would you relate this segment to the prece ing ones of the fourteenth chapter?

_____

Paragraph Analysis

15:1-4

1. Record the subject of each of the three par of the paragraph:

15:1,2 _____

15:3 _____

15:4 _____

2. What two fruits come of our trying to pleas our weaker Christian brothers (15:2)?

_____

Compare "edification" (v. 2) with "weaknesse (v. 1). _____

3. Pleasing our "neighbors" may be costly to u What did it cost Christ? _____

4. What four fruits come of the ministry of Scripture? _____
_____
_____
_____

15:5-6
1. Relate verse 5a to verse 4.
_____
_____

2. Relate this paragraph to verse 7. Observe among other things the references to God's glory. (Note where this appears on the survey chart.)
_____
_____

15:7-13
1. How do verses 8-12 relate to the opening verse 7? _____
_____

2. Record two reasons why Christ became a servant to the Jews (15:8,9).
_____
_____

3. Verse 13 is the concluding verse of the body of the epistle (1:18–15:13). How does it serve that function? _____
_____

Related Verses
Isa. 11:10 _____
_____
Matt. 12:21 _____
_____
Rom. 3:29 _____
_____
1 Cor. 10:33 _____
_____
Gal. 3:28 _____
_____
1 Thess. 5:12-15 _____
_____
2 Tim. 3:16 _____
_____
Heb. 12:2 _____
_____

INTERPRETATIONS
1. "Reproaches" (15:3). NIV translates the Greek word as "insults."
2. Why did Paul insert verse 4 where it is?

3. Which of the following paraphrases represents the intent of 15:5-6:
    (a) May God grant you unity so that you may glorify Him.
    (b) May God grant you unity so that you may glorify Him *with one voice*.
4. Does each quote of 15:9-12 support Paul's point of 15:9a? If so, how? _____
_____
_____

5. Reflect on how these words of 15:13 are related to each other, in the experience of the believer: hope, joy, peace, faith, power. Record some of your thoughts. _____
_____
_____
_____

APPLICATIONS
1. The Scriptures minister to the needs of *all* believers, weak and strong. How are weak Christians helped, according to 15:4? Do you know of any weaker Christian to whom you could minister the Word, for his help and edification? Why not try to make that contact before the week is over, or better yet, today.
2. In your own mind try listening to the sounds of two groups: one is discussing and arguing about what activities Christians should not engage in on Sunday afternoon; and the other group is sharing in testimony time, in warm fellowship, how God has been using His Word to help them in their Christian walk. Compare these two groups with what Paul prays for in 15:6b. Here is how someone has commented on this: "When the Church glorifies such a God with one heart and one mouth, it will have transcended all the troubles of Chapter 14."

Summary of Passage
Strong Christians should bear the failings of the weak, to please them and build them up. That is how Christ went about His life and ministry.

All of us should accept one another, even as Christ has accepted us, in order to bring praise to God. Christ became a servant of the Jews, and in so doing He confirmed the Father's promises to the patriarchs, and made possible the Gentiles' glorying in Him for His mercy.

Memory Verses   15:5-6

Looking Ahead
Paul begins the more personal part of his letter, writing here about his ministry to Gentiles, such as the church at Rome.

EPILOGUE
15:14—16:27

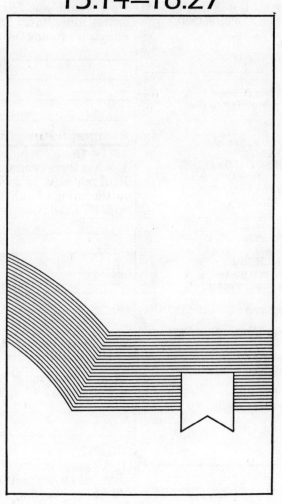

SETTING At this point Paul begins the last part of his letter, the EPILOGUE (see survey chart), which contains various personal notes, such as testimony and greeting.

Book of Romans: GOD'S SALVATION FOR SINNER

P R O L O G U E	NEED OF SALVATION	WAY OF SALVATION	LIFE OF SALVATION	SCOPE OF SALVATION	SERVICES OF SALVATION	
		DOCTRINAL			PRACTICAL	
	GOD'S POWER	GOD'S GRACE	GOD'S HOLINESS	GOD'S SOVEREIGNTY	GOD'S GLORY	
1:1	1:18	3:21	6:1	9:1	12:1	15

PREACHER OF THE GOSPEL

14 And concerning you, my BRETHREN,
    I myself also am convinced
    that you yourselves are
    (1) full of GOODNESS,
    (2) filled with ALL KNOWLEDGE, and
    (3) able also to admonish one another.
15   But I have written
    (1) very boldly to you on some points,
    (2) so as to remind you again,
    because of the GRACE
    that was GIVEN me from GOD
16   to be
    (1) a minister of CHRIST JESUS to the GENTILES,
    (2) ministering as a priest the GOSPEL of GOD,
    that my OFFERING of the GENTILES
        might become acceptable,
        sanctified by the HOLY SPIRIT.

THIS LETTER (purpose)

17 Therefore
        in CHRIST JESUS I have found reason
        for boasting in things pertaining to God.
18 For I will not presume
        to speak of anything
        except what CHRIST has accomplished
                    THROUGH ME,
    (1) resulting in the OBEDIENCE of the GENTILES
                    by WORD and DEED
19 (2) in the POWER of SIGNS and WONDERS,
    (3) in the POWER of the SPIRIT;
    so that
    (a) from Jerusalem and
    (b) round about as far as Illyricum
        I HAVE FULLY PREACHED
            THE GOSPEL OF CHRIST.
20 And thus I aspired to preach the gospel,
        not where CHRIST was already named,
        that I might not build
                    upon another man's FOUNDATION;
21 but as it is written,
    "(1) THEY who had no news of HIM SHALL SEE,
    and
    (2) THEY who have not heard
            SHALL UNDERSTAND."   [Isa. 52:15]
22 For this reason
        I have often been hindered
                    from COMING TO YOU.

DELAYED VISIT (reason)

OBSERVATIONS

Key Words and Phrases

15:14 "full of goodness" _____
    15 _____
    16 _____
    17 _____
    18 _____
    19 _____
    29 _____
    31 _____

others: _____
_____

Segment Survey

Note that the segment is divided into two paragraphs. Scan the text and observe the reasons for the outline as it appears on the textual recreation chart. This segment is mainly about: Paul, the church at Rome, or all Gentiles?

_____

How would you describe Paul's feelings as he writes these lines? Record at least five different adjectives in answering this.

_____
_____
_____
_____

Paragraph Analysis

15:14-16
1. What three commendations of his readers does Paul make (v. 14)? How is each of these relate to the things Paul has written throughout the epistle? Cite examples.

(1) _____
_____

(2) _____
_____

(3) _____
_____

2. Why did Paul write the letter?

_____

Observe the tone of modesty as he writes.
3. How do verses 15b-16 relate to that purpose?

_____
_____

15:17-22
1. A casual reader of verse 17-19 may conclude that Paul was vainly conceited in his "boasting. What are your impressions?

_____

In answering this, note how the phrase "in Christ Jesus" is related to the "boasting" (15:17). NI reads, "I glory in Christ Jesus in my service to God." Also, note the intention of the statement "what Christ has accomplished through me" (15:18). What was Paul's part (15:19b)?

_____

2. What does verse 20 reveal about Paul's character? _____
_____
_____

3. Why had Paul not yet visited the church at Rome? _____
_____
_____
_____

Related Verses

Acts 9:15 ff. _____
_____

Acts 15:12 _____
_____

2 Cor. 3:5 _____
_____

2 Cor. 10:15 ff. _____
_____

Gal. 1:9 _____
_____

1 Thess. 1:5 _____
_____

Heb. 5:1 _____
_____

INTERPRETATIONS

1. "Ministering as a priest" (15:16). The words "minister," "priest," and "offering" relate to Hebrew worship. The primary ministry of a priest was to be the sinner's intercessor before God, offering sacrifices acceptable to Him. Paul here uses those metaphors to describe his ministry to the Gentiles: "to be a minister of Christ Jesus to the Gentiles with the priestly duty of proclaiming the gospel of God, so that the Gentiles might become an offering acceptable to God, sanctified by the Holy Spirit" (15:16, NIV).

2. "Jerusalem...Illyricum" (15:19). A look at a map shows that Paul was thinking of the east-west limits: from Jerusalem in the east to Illyricum (present-day Yugoslavia) in the west. Illyricum bordered the northwest corner of Macedonia. Directly west, across the Adriatic Sea, was Italy and Rome, where Paul now had his sights.

3. "Not where Christ was already named" (15:20). The word "named" means "known." The harvest field of lost souls was almost boundless to begin with, without duplicating evangelistic ministries at this time. So Paul's policy was to pioneer in the areas where Christ had not yet been proclaimed. (Cf. 2 Cor. 10:15-17.)

APPLICATIONS

1. What spiritual traits would you look for in the lives of members of a Christian church today? Write a list, and compare it with what is known from this passage about the church at Rome.

_____
_____
_____
_____
_____
_____
_____
_____
_____
_____
_____

2. Paul's example as a witness for Christ is unmatched in the New Testament. In your own words write a list of those things revealed in the passage which made him so effective. Then check all of these against your own life and service for the Lord. Where do you need to grow—and maybe even begin? Share these things with each other in your group discussion. (TBS#7)

Summary of Passage

Paul commends the Christians at Rome for their spiritual character and maturity. He tells them that he has written the letter as a reminder of important matters, because his desire is to present to God a group of Gentile believers who are very pleasing to Him.

Paul is grateful for everything which Christ has accomplished through him thus far, in the ministry of the gospel, and his sights are now on a forthcoming visit to Rome.

A Memory Verse   15:14

Looking Ahead

Paul indicates what his next travel plans are, including a visit to the church at Rome.

SETTING The preceding passage was a summary of Paul's ministry to the Gentiles up until the time of writing. Now he rehearses his plan to visit Rome on his way to Spain.

Book of Romans: GOD'S SALVATION FOR SINNER

P R O L O G U E	NEED OF SALVATION	WAY OF SALVATION	LIFE OF SALVATION	SCOPE OF SALVATION	SERVICES OF SALVATION	E P I L O G U E
			DOCTRINAL		PRACTICAL	
	GOD'S POWER	GOD'S GRACE	GOD'S HOLINESS	GOD'S SOVEREIGNTY	GOD'S GLORY	
1:1	1:18	3:21	6:1	9:1	12:1	15:

LONGING FOR FELLOWSHIP

23 But now,
   (1) with no further place for me in these regions,
   (2) and since I have had **for many years**
         a longing to come to you,
24 [I plan to do so] whenever I go to Spain
   —for **I hope to see you** in passing,
   and **to be helped** on my way there **by you**,
   when I have first **enjoyed your company**
            for a while—
25 But now,
     I am going to JERUSALEM
        SERVING THE SAINTS.
26 For MACEDONIA and ACHAIA
    have been **pleased** to **make a contribution**
     for the poor
       among the **saints** in JERUSALEM.
27 Yes, they were **pleased** to do so,
   and they are INDEBTED TO THEM.
  For if the GENTILES
   have **shared** in their spiritual things,
  they are **indebted**
   to **minister** to them also in material things.

MISSION TO JERUSALEM

28 Therefore,
    when I have **finished** this,
    and have put my seal on THIS FRUIT of THEIRS,
   I will go on by way of you to SPAIN.
29 And I **know**
   that when I COME TO YOU,
     I WILL COME
      in the **fullness**
      of the **blessing** of CHRIST.

TRIP TO ROME

30 Now **I URGE YOU, BRETHREN,**
   (1) by our LORD JESUS CHRIST and
   (2) by the **love** of the SPIRIT
  to
    STRIVE together with me
    IN YOUR PRAYERS to GOD FOR ME,
31 (1) that I may be DELIVERED
    from those who are **disobedient** in JUDEA, and
   (2) that my SERVICE for JERUSALEM
    may prove **acceptable** to the saints;
32 (3) so that I may COME TO YOU
      IN JOY
      BY THE WILL OF GOD
   (4) and find REFRESHING REST in your company.
33   NOW the GOD OF PEACE
        BE WITH YOU ALL.
                    Amen.

PRAYER REQUESTS

OBSERVATIONS

Key Words and Phrases

15:23 "longing" _____
   24_____
   25_____
   26_____
   27_____
   30_____
   31_____

   32_____

others: _____
_____

Segment Survey

Follow the outline on the chart, as you read the three paragraphs. How is the third paragraph different from the first two?

Compare these different groups in the passage.

(1) Gentiles of Macedonia and Achaia
_____

(2) residents of Judea _____

(3) saints in Jerusalem _____

(4) church at Rome_____

Does Paul write anything about the residents of Spain?_____

Paragraph Analysis

15:23-27

1. Read the core of the paragraph, which is verse 25. The phrase "but now" picks up the similar phrase of verse 23. (Note: in the textual re-creation, "but" reads as "But," and the statement "I plan to do so" [NIV] is added to complete the grammatical sentence.)

2. Relate "but now" of verse 23 to 15:22.
_____
_____

3. How do key words in verses 23-24 set the tone for the segment? _____
_____

4. Why was it fitting for Paul to deliver the offering? _____
_____

5. Account for the pleasure and the indebtedness (15:26-27)._____
_____

15:28-29

1. What do you think is meant by "have put my seal on this fruit of theirs" (15:28)?
_____
_____

2. Read the last phrase of verse 29. Do you think Paul means Christ's blessing for him, or through him to the church, or both? Read carefully what Paul had written earlier in the letter, in 1:10-15.
_____
_____

15:30-33

. Record the strong words of verse 30.

_____

_____

_____

. Note the references to the three Persons of the Trinity.

. What are Paul's four prayer requests?

. _____

. _____

. _____

. _____

Iow do these requests account for the words of erse 30, "strive in your prayers"?

_____

_____

Related Verses

Acts 9:13-16 _____

_____

Acts 19:21-22 _____

_____

Acts 21–28 _____

_____

_____

Cor. 9:7-14 _____

_____

Cor. 16:1-4 _____

_____

Cor. 8–9 _____

INTERPRETATIONS

. "With no further place for me in these regions" 15:23). How do you think Paul knew this?

_____

_____

. "To be helped on my way there by you" (15:24). t was customary among the churches to provide oom and board to visiting evangelists during heir stay, and then to pay the expenses of the ourney to the next place of ministry.
. The "Gentiles have shared in their [Israel's] piritual things" (15:27). The gospel of salvation ame to the Gentile world via the Jewish world, o Paul identifies this as an indebtedness on the art of Gentiles. The contribution was not pay-nent for the glad tidings but an expression of oncern and assistance along with thanks for the ews' beings God's channel of the gospel message.
. "Have put my seal on this fruit of theirs" 15:28). NIV translates this statement, "have nade sure that they have received this fruit."

APPLICATIONS

. What do you learn from Paul about the love f the brethren? How can you explain such a deep onging to see the Christians at Rome?

_____

_____

2. What does this passage teach about helping the poor? How often have you participated in this kind of ministry? _____

_____

_____

3. Paul believed in prayer, and in praying one for another. Write down some important things from 15:30-32 which you can apply to your own life. (TBS#4) _____

_____

_____

_____

_____

_____

_____

_____

_____

_____

Summary of Passage

Paul writes again how much he longs to see the Christians at Rome. He expects to see them on a journey that he plans to take from Jerusalem to Spain. Right now he is on his way to Jerusalem, bringing an offering from Macedonia and Achaia to the poor among the saints. He urges his brothers in the Lord to pray earnestly that God will deliver him from troublemakers of Judea when he arrives in Jerusalem, that his ministry in Jerusalem may prove acceptable, and that his visit at Rome will be a joyous and refreshing one.

A Memory Verse   15:30-32

Looking Ahead

Pual and others with him send many personal greetings to the friends at Rome.

SETTING Paul is nearing the conclusion of his letter, so he takes this opportunity to send along personal greetings to various members of the church at Rome.

Book of Romans: GOD'S SALVATION FOR SINNE

P R O L O G U E	NEED OF SALVATION	WAY OF SALVATION	LIFE OF SALVATION	SCOPE OF SALVATION	SERVICES OF SALVATION	
		DOCTRINAL			PRACTICAL	
	GOD'S POWER	GOD'S GRACE	GOD'S HOLINESS	GOD'S SOVEREIGNTY	GOD'S GLORY	
1:1	1:18	3:21	6:1	9:1	12:1	1:

FELLOW-WORKERS IN CHRIST

1 I commend to you
    our sister Phoebe
  who is a SERVANT of the church which is
                at Cenchrea;
2 that you receive her
  (1) in the Lord
  (2) in a manner worthy of the SAINTS,
  and that you help her
    in whatever matter she may HAVE NEED of you;
  for she herself has also been a HELPER
  (1) of many, and
  (2) of myself as well.

ONE SERVANT

3 Greet Prisca and Aquila
  my FELLOW WORKERS in CHRIST JESUS,
4   WHO for my life
      RISKED THEIR OWN NECKS,
  to whom not only do I give **thanks,**
    but also **all the churches of the GENTILES;**

TWO FELLOW WORKERS

5 also greet the church that is in their house.
  Greet Epaenetus my BELOVED,
  who is the FIRST CONVERT TO CHRIST from Asia.
6 Greet Mary, who has **worked hard** for you.
7 Greet Andronicus and Junias,
    my KINSMEN, and my FELLOW-PRISONERS
  who
  (1) are **outstanding** among the apostles,
  who also
  (2) **were IN CHRIST before me.**
8 Greet Ampliatus, my BELOVED in THE LORD.
9 Greet Urbanus, **our** FELLOW WORKER in CHRIST,
    and Stachys my BELOVED.
10 Greet Apelles, the APPROVED in CHRIST.
  Greet those who are of the household
            of Aristobulus.
11 Greet Herodian, my KINSMAN.
  Greet those of the household of Narcissus,
        who are in the LORD.
12 Greet Tryphaena and Tryphosa,
        WORKERS in the LORD.
  Greet Persis the BELOVED,
    who has WORKED **HARD** in the LORD.
13 Greet
  (1) Rufus, a CHOICE MAN in the LORD,
  also
  (2) his mother and
  (3) mine.
14 Greet Asyncritus, Phlegon, Hermes, Patrobas,
    Hermas and the **BRETHREN with them.**
15 Greet Philologus and Julia,
    Nereus and his sister, and Olympas,
  and all the **SAINTS who are with them.**

MANY BRETHREN

16 GREET ONE ANOTHER WITH A HOLY KISS.
  All the **churches of Christ**
        greet you.

ALL THE CHURCHES

OBSERVATIONS

Key Words and Phrases

16:1 "servant of the church" _____
  2 _____

3 _____
4 _____
5 _____
6 _____
7 _____
8 _____
others: _____
_____

Segment Survey

A quick glance at the passage shows one ke repeated word. What is it? _____
What is the main purpose of the sixteen verses?
_____

We do not know what determined the *order* Paul's greetings. But it helps our study if w identify groups of verses, arbitrary as this ma be. Note that the segment is divided into thre paragraphs, following a quantitative sequen of 1, 2, and many.

All of the verses of the third paragraph are *sho* greetings. What is the one exception?
_____

Count on the chart how many women Paul gree by name. Then count the number of men named.

Someone has called this passage "the picture ga lery of New Testament saints." (Cf. the Old Te tament gallery in Hebrews 11.)

Paragraph Analysis

16:1-2
1. Was Phoebe part of the Roman church fellov ship yet? What are her credentials?
_____
_____

2. What are Paul's two requests concerning her?
_____
_____

3. Why do you think Paul wrote about Phoeb first? _____
_____

16:3-4
1. How does Paul praise Aquila and Priscilla?
_____
_____
_____

(Read Acts 18:2,26; 1 Corinthians 16:19;

2 Timothy 4:19.)
2. Why do you think Paul greeted this pair first?

_____

_____

16:5-15
1. On a separate sheet of paper list the Christians at Rome. Use four columns, with these headings (examples given):

Name v.5	Title	Service	Other I.D.
Epaenetus	my beloved		first convert ...from Asia

2. What phrase does Paul use often in the titles and identifications?_____

_____

3. Which names does he single out, and why?

_____

_____

4. What is the tone of this passage?

_____

16:16
How does this verse serve as a summary of the "greeting-card"?_____

_____

Related Verses
Mark 15:21 _____

_____

Acts 18:18_____

_____

Rom. 9:3 _____

_____

Phil. 2:29_____

_____

1 Thess. 5:26 _____

_____

1 Tim. 3:10-11 _____

_____

1 Peter 5:14_____

_____

INTERPRETATIONS
1. "Servant of the church which is at Cenchrea" (16:1). Phoebe was probably on her way to Rome. Some think she may have delivered Paul's letter to the Christians there. What women in this passage (16:1-16) does Paul identify as *workers*?

_____

_____

2. "Helper" (16:2). Compare 1 Corinthians 12:28, regarding the gift of helps.
3. "The church that is in their house" (16:5). Rather than meeting in one large meeting place in Rome, the Christians met in small groups, mostly in private homes. Note especially the collective phrases of verses 14 and 15.
4. "Holy kiss" (16:16). Peter refers to this as a "kiss of love" (1 Peter 5:14). This was the usual Eastern manner of greeting, and is still a live custom.

APPLICATIONS
1. Almost one third of the names of this greeting are those of women, and Paul cites many of these as being workers in the church. How should this be applied to the Christian scene today, concerning the Lord's vineyard? Discuss this with your group._____

_____

_____

_____

_____

_____

2. God has a place and service for every believer in the local fellowships of Christians, and He does not look for quantity but quality in service. What does this passage teach about quality? What qualities do you aspire to have and consecrate to the Lord?

Summary of Passage
Paul commends to the saints at Rome a sister and helper in the Lord, Phoebe, who is on her way to that city. He greets the many Christians who are worshiping together in various homes, calling each by name and commending them for their place in the Lord's vineyard.

He also sends greetings from all the churches of Christ scattered throughout the empire.

Memory Verses   16:3-4
Looking Ahead
Paul concludes his letter with words of caution, greetings from his co-workers, and a final doxology.

SETTING These are Paul's last words in his letter to the Christians at Rome. After the last word, *"Amen,"* there is nothing more to say at this time.

Book of Romans: GOD'S SALVATION FOR SINNER

P R O L O G U E	NEED OF SALVATION	WAY OF SALVATION	LIFE OF SALVATION	SCOPE OF SALVATION	SERVICES OF SALVATION	
		DOCTRINAL			PRACTICAL	
	GOD'S POWER	GOD'S GRACE	GOD'S HOLINESS	GOD'S SOVEREIGNTY	GOD'S GLORY	
1:1	1:18	3:21	6:1	9:1	12:1	15

TO GOD BE THE GLORY

17 Now I **urge you,** BRETHREN,
    keep your eye
  on those who cause **dissensions** and **hindrances**
    contrary to THE TEACHING
      WHICH YOU LEARNED,
        and turn away from them.
18 For such men are SLAVES
    NOT of our LORD CHRIST
    BUT of their own **appetites;**
  and by their smooth and flattering speech
    they **deceive**
      the hearts of the unsuspecting.
19 For the report of your **obedience**
            has reached to all;
  therefore I am REJOICING OVER YOU,
      but I want you to be
  (1) WISE in what is **good,** and
  (2) INNOCENT in what is **evil.**
20   And the GOD OF PEACE
  will soon **CRUSH SATAN** under your feet.
    The GRACE of our LORD JESUS
      be with you.

(margin: WARNING)

21 Timothy my FELLOW WORKER greets you;
  and so do
    Lucius and Jason and Sosipater, my KINSMEN.
22   [I, Tertius, who write this letter,
      greet you in the Lord.]
23 Gaius,
  HOST to me and to the whole church,
  greets you.
  Erastus, the city treasurer greets you,
  and Quartus, the brother.
24   The GRACE of our LORD JESUS CHRIST
    be with you all. Amen.

(margin: GREETINGS)

25 NOW TO HIM who is ABLE
  to ESTABLISH YOU
  (1) according to my GOSPEL
      and the PREACHING of JESUS CHRIST,
  (2) according to the **revelation** of
    the MYSTERY which
      (a) has been **kept secret**
        for **long ages past,** but
26 now
      (b) is **manifested** and
      —by the Scriptures of the prophets,
      —according to the commandment
          of the ETERNAL GOD,
  has been **made known** to all the nations,
      —leading to obedience of faith;
27   TO THE ONLY WISE GOD
    through JESUS CHRIST,
      [to whom]
      BE THE GLORY FOREVER.
        Amen.

(margin: DOXOLOGY)

OBSERVATIONS

Key Words and Phrases

16:17 _____ "keep your eye on" _____

  17 _____

  18 _____

---

19 _____

20 _____

21 _____

25 _____

27 _____

others: _____

_____

Segment Survey

Paul's conclusion to the letter contains thre parts. Read the three paragraphs, and recor below the main purpose of each:

16:17-20 _____

16:21-24 _____

16:25-27 _____

Compare the beginning and end of the segment.

_____

Would you say that most of the segment is pos

tive or negative? _____

Which paragraph is mostly doctrinal?

_____

Before moving along in your study of this uni read the opening seven verses of the epistle (Un 1). Compare this with the epistle's conclusion

(16:17-27). _____

Paragraph Analysis

16:17-20

1. How does Paul describe the trouble-makers

their deeds _____

their motivations _____

their methods _____

their victims _____

their ultimate destiny _____

2. What are Paul's three commands to the Chris tians concerning these trouble-makers?

v. 17 _____

v. 17 _____

v. 19 _____

3. How does Paul commend his readers in verse

19a? _____

Why then does he write the remainder of th

verse (v. 19b)? _____

_____

16:21-24

How is this paragraph mainly different fro

16:1-16? _____

_____

16:25-27

1. What is this paragraph mainly about (choose one): promise to the readers; praise to God; preaching of doctrine; encouragement to the readers?

2. State the core of the doxology in five words of the text: "To_____."

3. The doxology encourages the Christian from two perspectives: past and present. In your own words, identify these:

PAST _____

PRESENT_____

Related Verses

Matt. 7:15-16_____

_____

Matt. 10:16 _____

_____

1 Cor. 14:20_____

_____

Gal. 1:6-9_____

_____

Eph. 3:1-7 _____

_____

Phil. 3:19_____

_____

1 Tim. 6:3-5_____

_____

INTERPRETATIONS

1. "Dissensions and hindrances" (16:17). NIV translates "hindrances" as "obstacles." How are these obstacles different from the ones discussed earlier in 14:13 ff.?_____

_____

Are the trouble-makers of 16:18 Christians? Support your answer from the text._____

2. *The Living Bible* paraphrases 16:19b: "I want you always to remain very clear about what is right, and to stay innocent of any wrong."

3. "I Tertius, who write this letter" (16:22). Tertius was Paul's scribe, or secretary, who wrote in clear penmanship what Paul had first composed.

4. "Revelation of the mystery" (16:25). Mystery is something formerly unknown (e.g., in Old Testament times) until revealed to the initiated (e.g., revelation by Christ). Read Ephesians 3:4-6. In the context of that passage Paul wrote that "this mystery is that through the gospel the Gentiles are heirs together with Israel, members together of one body, and sharers together in the promise in Christ Jesus" (Eph. 3:6, NIV).

5. "To whom" (16:27). The phrase doesn't fit the grammatical construction of a sentence. The NIV translation omits the phrase, in this reading: "to the only wise God be glory forever through Jesus Christ Amen." A full interpretation would be the combination: "To God *and* to Jesus Christ be the glory...."

APPLICATIONS

1. Satan is the master and motivator of all trouble-makers, so it does not surprise us that Paul names Satan in verse 20 in the context of the dissensions and hindrances. Observe that Paul's instruction involves (1) our part, "keep your eye on" and "turn away" and (2) God's part, He "will soon crush Satan." Compare this with similar scriptures which tell us bluntly, "Stay away" (e.g., James 4:7). Have you experienced this way of victory in your own experience? Your discussion group may want to share testimonies about this.

2. As you tarry over the last paragraph of Romans (16:25-27) in this concluding study of the epistle, what truths of the doxology inspire and challenge you? Thank Him again for reaching down and drawing you to Himself, and for using you as a witness of the gospel.

Summary of Passage

Paul alerts all Christians not to be deceived by the crafty ways of trouble-makers who cause divisions and hindrances in Christian fellowships. Their doom is sealed, but Christians need to watch out.

After sending greetings from his co-workers, Paul concludes his epistle with a grand doxology to God who is able to establish His people by the gospel and the preaching of Jesus Christ—TO GOD BE THE GLORY!

A Memory Verse   16:20

In Conclusion

What are your impressions of the book of Romans, and how would you evaluate it? People who have read and studied this epistle cannot find words sufficient to describe its worth. Here are some reactions:

"The most profound book in existence."
—Coleridge

"Cathedral of the Christian faith"
—Godet

"The chief part of the New Testament"
—Luther

Before you move on to studies of another book of the Bible, why not review your studies in Romans, to recapture and solidify the highlights of the epistle? This will help you remember this divine masterpiece for years to come. One method of review is to read the surveys and summaries included in each unit of this study guide. Also memorize the survey chart, so that you can think through the progression of the epistle from beginning to end.

SELECTED SOURCES
FOR FURTHER BIBLE STUDY

Bright, Bill. *The Discipleship Series*. San Bernardino: Here's Life Publishers, 1980.

_____. *Ten Basic Steps Toward Christian Maturity*. San Bernardino: Here's Life Publishers, 1980.

Bruce, F. F. *The Epistle of Paul to the Romans*. London: Tyndale, 1963.

_____. *The Letters of Paul: An Expanded Paraphrase*. Grand Rapids: Eerdmans, 1965.

Chafer, L. S. *He That Is Spiritual*. Grand Rapids: Zondervan, 1918. Discussion of sanctification.

Davidson, F., and Martin, Ralph P. "Romans." In *The New Bible Commentary*. Grand Rapids: Eerdmans, 1963.

Erdman, Charles R. *The Epistle of Paul to the Romans*. Philadelphia: Westminster, 1942.

Goodwin, Frank J. *A Harmony of the Life of St. Paul*. 3rd ed. Grand Rapids: Baker, 1953.

Hiebert, D. Edmond. *An Introduction to the Pauline Epistles*. Chicago: Moody, 1954.

Hodge, Charles. *Commentary on the Epistle to the Romans*. New York: Armstrong, 1890.

Jensen, Irving L. *Enjoy Your Bible*. Chicago: Moody, 1969. Discussion of various Bible study methods, including textual re-creation.

_____. *Independent Bible Study*. Chicago: Moody, 1963. Introduction to inductive Bible study and the analytical chart method.

_____. *Romans* (Bible Self-Study Guide). Chicago: Moody, 1969.

Lenski, R.C.H. *The Interpretation of St. Paul's Epistle to the Romans*. Columbus, Ohio: Wartburg, 1945.

Mickelsen, A. Berkeley. "The Epistle to the Romans." In *The Wycliffe Bible Commentary*. Chicago: Moody, 1962.

Newell, William R. *Romans Verse by Verse*. Chicago: Moody, 1948.

Stalker, James. *The Life of St. Paul*. Rev. ed. Westwood, N.J.: Revell, 1912.

Thomas, Robert L., ed. *The New American Standard Exhaustive Concordance of the Bible*. Nashville: Holman, 1981.

Vine, W. E. *An Expository Dictionary of New Testament Words*. Westwood, N.J.: Revell, 1961.

Walvoord, John F. *Israel in Prophecy*. Grand Rapids: Zondervan, 1962.

Wuest, Kenneth S. *Romans in the Greek New Testament*. Grand Rapids: Eerdmans, 195?.

REVIEW NOTES OF ROMANS

REVIEW NOTES OF ROMANS

REVIEW NOTES OF ROMANS

REVIEW NOTES OF ROMANS

DO-IT-YOURSELF BIBLE STUDIES FROM
IRVING JENSEN

Outstanding resources for comprehensive Bible study! These do-it-yourself commentaries feature thought-provoking questions, suggestions for discussion, and thorough explanations—profitable and enjoyable for both individual and group study.

Quantity		The Complete New Testament		Total
____	ISBN 0-89840-037-6	Matthew	$6.95	____
____	ISBN 0-89840-035-X	Mark	$6.95	____
____	ISBN 0-89840-096-1	Luke	$6.95	____
____	ISBN 0-89840-051-1	John	$6.95	____
____	ISBN 0-89840-066-X	Acts	$6.95	____
____	ISBN 0-89840-036-8	Romans	$6.95	____
____	ISBN 0-89840-116-X	1 Corinthians	$6.95	____
____	ISBN 0-89840-164-X	2 Corinthians/Galatians	$6.95	____
____	ISBN 0-89840-060-0	General Epistles	$6.95	____
____	ISBN 0-89840-180-1	Prison Epistles/1 & 2 Thessalonians	$6.95	____
____	ISBN 0-89840-077-5	Hebrews/Pastoral Epistles	$6.95	____
____	ISBN 0-89840-081-3	Revelation	$6.95	____

Selected Old Testament Studies

____	ISBN 0-89840-282-4	Genesis	$7.95	____
____	ISBN 0-89840-202-6	Psalms	$7.95	____

Character Studies

____	ISBN 0-89840-215-8	David: A Man After God's Own Heart	$4.95	____
____	ISBN 0-89840-269-7	Ruth and Mary: Women of Courage	$4.95	____

Indicate product(s) desired above. Fill out below.
Send to:

HERE'S LIFE PUBLISHERS, INC.
P. O. Box 1576
San Bernardino, CA 92402-1576

NAME _____

ADDRESS _____

STATE _____ ZIP _____

☐ Payment (check or money order only) included

☐ Visa   ☐ Mastercard # _____

Expiration Date_____Signature_____

FOR FASTER SERVICE
CALL TOLL FREE: 1-800-950-4457

ORDER TOTAL $_____

SHIPPING and
HANDLING $_____
($1.50 for one book,
$0.50 for each additional.
Do not exceed $4.00.)

APPLICABLE
SALES TAX
(CA, 6%) $_____

TOTAL DUE $_____
PAYABLE IN US FUNDS.
(No cash orders accepted.)

RO 036-8

Your Christian bookstore should have these in stock. If not, use this "Shop-by-Mail" form.
PLEASE ALLOW 2 TO 4 WEEKS FOR DELIVERY.
PRICES SUBJECT TO CHANGE WITHOUT NOTICE.